Dilemmas in Dealing wit

About the series 'Books for the Concerned Citizen'

Leveraging the diverse expertise of its members in the subject domains and in publishing, the TERI Alumni Association is publishing a series of books on topics related to energy, resources, and the environment. The idea is to share information and, even more important, critical insights and understanding, with citizens who are keen to know more about some of the critical issues facing society and the world today but are lost in the deluge of information.

Our target audience is educated adults who are concerned about topical issues but lack the understanding to make sense of what they read or watch in the mass media—the series aims to equip them with conceptual tools and essential information not only to enrich their understanding but also to encourage them to act and thereby, albeit indirectly, further the UN Sustainable Development Goals.

The topics to be covered in the series and their respective subject-matter-specialist authors are listed below.

- **Rooftop solar***: Suneel Deambi and Shirish Garud
- **Coal***: Rakesh Kacker
- **Sustainable buildings***: Mili Majumdar and Minni Sastry
- **Nutraceuticals***: Mayurika Goel
- **Electricity***: Sanjeev S Ahluwalia
- **Clean transport***: Shri Prakash and Sharif Qamar
- **Energy efficiency**: Ajay Mathur and Leher Thadani
- **Climate change**: Manish Shrivastava
  already published and available for purchase

The publication of this series is financially supported by the Shakti Sustainable Energy Foundation. All books, being printed and marketed by TERI will be published latest by November 2022.

Dilemmas in Dealing with Climate Change in India

Manish Shrivastava

ISBN: 978-81-950776-7-0

Suggested citation
Shrivastava M. 2022. *Dilemmas in Dealing with Climate Change in India.* New Delhi: TERI Alumni Association. 68 pp.

TERI Alumni Association
Administrative Wing, TERI
Darbari Seth Block (ground floor)
Habitat Place
Lodhi Road
New Delhi – 110 003

Price Rs 299/-
For sales queries, please contact us at
Nand K Yadav, Assistant Manager - Sales
The Energy and Resources Institute (TERI Press)
Darbari Seth Block, Habitat Place
Lodhi Road, New Delhi – 110 003

+91 97 173 56537 or +91 (0) 11 7110 2100 or 2468 2100
nandkumar.yadav@teri.res.in or teripress@teri.res.in
Fax +91 2468 2144 or 2468 2145

THE ENERGY AND RESOURCES INSTITUTE
Creating Innovative Solutions for a Sustainable Future

For more information, contact
Manish Shrivastava (manish.shrivastava@teri.res.in)

CONTENTS

Foreword   vii

Preface   xi

Introduction   1

Climate change: a scientific perspective   3

How should India be concerned about climate change?   9

India and the global politics of climate change   14

The landscape of adaption policy   19

Climate change mitigation in India   24

The capacity challenge to implementation   31

Social objectives and climate policy   36

India's net-zero target: the context and road ahead   41

A just transition: difficult choices   46

The not-so-changing landscape of climate governance   53

Conclusions   63

Bibliography   65

FOREWORD

This book will please those who believe that fixing the problem
of climate change is not only about eliminating carbon from the
economic system but equally, and perhaps more importantly,
about sustainable development and climate justice. The book
will therefore surprise those who fail to take into account the
challenges to social and economic development that confront a
growing society.

In any discourse on climate change, one usually comes across
two kinds of believers and proponents: the die-hard evangelists
who swear by the perils of inaction and want policymakers to
make choices for ambitious mitigation of greenhouse gases' emissions, sometimes in complete disregard to the social and economic
consequences, and the climate sceptics who want to pursue a
resource-intensive and economically wasteful path of development
with no concern for future generations. Dr Manish Shrivastava's
book, *Dilemmas in Dealing with Climate Change in India*, is a re-
freshing departure from this tradition. He seeks to present the dilemmas of climate policy in a socially relevant context with deeper
understanding of practical choices for the stakeholders in India. In
this sense, his series of essays on climate dilemmas is a reminder
of the need to take a comprehensive view of public policy choices
in the context of climate change.

I have known Manish as a young professor who has taught
various aspects of climate change policy and sustainable
development to students at the TERI School of Advanced Studies.
The present book establishes his credibility as a committed
environmental researcher who is aware that climate change is
not a unidimensional problem. The book highlights the social,
economic, and governance issues that need to be necessarily dealt
with while coping with the problem. He also emphasizes that a
public debate on these issues must be carried out in a balanced

manner. He observes that there is need to promote a larger public conversation about climate change rather than propagate an academic prognosis.

On many occasions in my experience of international negotiations on climate change for over a decade I have been conscious of the lack of research material in respect of the social and economic dimensions of climate change in India and related policy dilemmas. Manish's book fills the gap and analyses the dynamics inherent in the efforts to address climate change in a growing society: the spectrum of issues he deals with includes several of them, such as vulnerability, adaptation, technology, capacity, resources, and governance.

The challenge of mitigation – reducing the emissions of greenhouse gases – usually receives greatest attention in a country's policy making. The challenge can be met by mobilizing technologies and resources at scale. Success on this front depends largely on how the finance is organized and technology is deployed on the required scale in the manufacturing and the service sectors. However, in a country such as India, adaptation to climate change remains a fundamental challenge. Constraints in terms of capacity, access to resources, livelihood, and community mobilization have much greater impact in dealing with climate change but cannot be overcome only with low-emission technologies. And a move away from carbon-heavy production and construction also has adverse impacts on communities. As Manish points out, even in promoting solar energy we need to be mindful of potential trade-offs between agriculture and renewable-energy plants in terms of land requirements. It is therefore important to understand the interplay of social and economic forces in the wake of policies aimed at mitigation. This book seeks to highlight such issues and presents the dilemmas in the wider context of development, capacity, and governance.

In dealing with policy dilemmas, Manish also draws attention to one issue that usually gets brushed under the carpet in global discourse on climate change, namely border adjustment of carbon taxes. In a globally integrated economy, environmental measures taken in one country can have adverse impacts on its trading partners as is evident from the border adjustment of carbon taxes being considered by the European Union or the regulation of access to energy supplies through political or administrative fiats as seen in the course of current Russia–Ukraine conflict. These measures taken in the name of environmental management are actually instruments to retain a competitive economic advantage. Legitimate global concerns on the aggravating climate crisis thus tend to create development constraints for societies that face the brunt of climate change.

It would not be out of place to mention that the institutional structure for climate governance in India is an area of concern. The framework is still evolving. Some efforts have been made to prepare and implement national missions on climate change. Many states in India are also implementing state-specific action plans on climate change but lack capacity and resources. Manish rightly presents this as a serious constraint in climate governance that needs to be tackled urgently.

In recent times, calls for the net-zero goal by mid-century and climate justice have gained a lot of currency at political level. However, achieving such goals requires a nuanced growth strategy for such growing economies as India. Manish is right to draw attention to the issue of just transition in this context and ask questions relating to technology and capacity.

Frequent dilemmas in devising public policies for a developing economy are quite natural. Each sector of economy suffers from some typical constraints when it comes to low-carbon development and choices related to mitigation or adaptation. Such constraints are unavoidable in the process of transition. However, it is critical to ensure that in this process we do not lose sight of the social and economic imperatives. This concern runs through Manish's book and forms the basis of his treatment of specific issues. I am confident that this publication will enrich the existing literature on climate policy in India and may even act as a guidebook to persons involved with making choices and implementing solutions at various levels.

R R Rashmi
Distinguished Fellow, TERI and
former Special Secretary,
November 2022
Government of India

PREFACE

When the TERI Alumni Association conceived the idea of
publishing a series of books on issues of contemporary relevance,
particularly around energy and environment, with a view to
reaching out to general readers, the proposal looked exciting,
and I committed myself to writing one on climate change readily
enough when Mr Amit Kumar requested me to do so. At that
point, about a year ago, it seemed relatively easy, given that I was
teaching courses on the economics, governance, and global politics
of climate change at TERI SAS, the TERI School of Advanced
Studies. It seemed easy enough to summarize the lectures and give
them the shape of a book. Yet, it turned out to be a difficult task
for three reasons.

The first reason was that the subject of climate change is vast
and complex. As I began to think about the content, the idea
that the topic could be presented within 60–70 pages started
increasingly to be one based on an ignorant person's confidence:
'Fools rush in where angels fear to tread', as the idiom has it.
Hence, it was necessary to select only some aspects of climate
change—easier said than done. The task was made more difficult
by the fact that a few themes that dominate the discourse on
climate change – energy efficiency, renewable energy, coal,
transport, and so on – were already the subject of separate books
in the series. It seemed as if lead characters from a classic play
have been taken off the stage.

The second reason was that it proved difficult to find a way
to communicate the complex technicalities of climate change to
general readers. In the classroom or in seminars, the audience is
aware at least to some extent of the key issues and committed to
putting in the required effort to understand the knottier issues of
the discourse. One can tell the story by building on a shared base
of information and premises. That is not the case with the target
audience of this series. There is no way one could know what the

readers already know about the subject or what they expect from such a book.

The third reason was to decide on the level of detail in writing: How much technical detail is necessary? To what extent should I insist on being technically precise? Would being too generic defeat the purpose? For someone who has engaged with the subject based entirely on the differences of perspectives on the nitty-gritty technical details of scientific facts and political interpretations for 15 years, this was not an easy task.

In search of a solution, I began reflecting on my own experiences in learning about climate change and teaching it to different audiences with whom I was engaged for only a few hours. It seemed that it is curiosity that drives engagement. Curiosity can come from different angles and perspectives, but all of them have one factor in common: one should be able to relate the content to something that one already knows or thinks about irrespective of whether the existing knowledge or thinking is right or wrong. It seemed reasonable, therefore, that the content should be such that it allows as many possible hooks for curiosity as climate change allows. Further, it also seemed right that a public discourse is always possible when it comes to public policy of a country, particularly when there is scope for debate.

Inviting readers to join the debate on climate policy dilemmas in India, therefore, seemed a useful pragmatic anchor in writing this book. In particular, engagements with the master's students of the Public Policy and Sustainable Development programme at TERI SAS offered useful insights. These students are mid-career government officials from different departments. They are not necessarily exposed to the nuances of climate change science and policy but have strong opinions and curiosity about the sectoral dimensions of climate change. Conducting a scientifically reasonable conversation with a diverse group was challenging but enriching. What always worked in those settings was to give the minimum technical details necessary to give any debate on public policy a touch and context of climate change. That is how this book was written: a compilation of opening statements to initiate conversation with excitable readers. That is what each section of this book is: an opening statement.

While writing this book, time and again I went back in time and was reminded of random, exciting, heated, and sometimes useless conversations I have had with many of my friends and colleagues about climate change. In particular, discussions with Prabhat Upadhyaya, Neha Pahuja, Ritu Mathur, Saurabh Bhardwaj, Prasoon Singh, Ritika Tiwari, Kavya Michael, Karan Mangotra, Aayushi Awasthi, Swati D'Souza, Suruchi Bhadwal, Gopal Sarangi, Abhijit Datey, and Sapan Thapar have been enriching over the years. When disagreements or unresolved issues propped up, I reached out to Dr Prodipto Ghosh, Ambassador Chandrashekhar Dasgupta, Dr Leena Srivastava, Mr Amit Kumar, Dr Ajay Mathur, Mr Surya Sethi, and Mr Girish Sethi for their perspective and their experience with public-policy engagements. These conversations have left a deeper imprint on much of what is written in this book.

I am extremely grateful to Mr R R Rashmi for writing the foreword to this book in a very short period of time. He has always been supportive, accessible, and candid about public policy challenges related to climate change in Indian context during my career as a climate policy researcher.

This book would not have been possible without the sensitive coordinating reminders and advice in these stressful times by Mr Rakesh Kacker and Dr Vibha Dhawan. I cannot thank them sufficiently without also offering my apologies for going off-schedule on several occasions. They have been extremely patient with me. So have been Mr Yateendra Joshi and Mr P K Jayanthan with their editorial support. It has always been a joyful experience to work with the team at TERI Press: Anupama Jauhary and Rajiv Sharma. Many thanks to them.

While writing this book, my wife, Malancha Chakrabarty, and my son, Bihan, made me realize that the questions of intragenerational and intergenerational equity are not just abstract concepts to be debated once a year at meetings of the Conference of Parties [to the UN Framework Convention on Climate Change, or COPs for short], but issues that demand sensitive choices to be made every day.

Introduction

It is now a well-accepted fact that climate change is a real problem that needs urgent global response. It is also a wicked problem in the sense that not only will it negatively affect the social and economic lives of people but also the measures that the world would take to address the threats posed by that problem may significantly impact those lives. Although the problem demands urgent and bold actions by countries – actions that might transform their infrastructure and economies – such actions, if taken in haste and without duly considering the societal contexts, will prove to be grossly unjust, perhaps undermining the moral reasoning itself that demands immediate action. For decades this has posed a major moral dilemma for policymakers across countries, namely whether to provide for and protect the well-being of people today or to protect the climate system for future generations. The fact that people today do not have access to equitable living standards further complicates this problem. The core climate policy dilemma, therefore, has been the intersectionality and competitive demands of intragenerational and intergenerational equity.

Climate change is a wicked problem also in its global versus national imperatives. On the one hand, it is a problem that requires everybody's cooperation in managing the global commons, a problem fraught with political posturing and arm twisting, twisted use of moral imperatives hiding the ugly face of international economic competitiveness. On the other hand, it is also a problem that each country has to solve for itself. Finding the right balance between developmental aspirations and the transition towards a climate-resilient low-carbon economy is not easy for a country in an internationally embedded economy. India has been in the eye of the storm in international climate negotiations, very often finding itself in the minority, defending the moral imperatives of a fair global climate response as well as the well-being of the larger community of the developing world.

Of course, the political and economic imperatives of national interests are integral material drivers of India's position in the negotiations related to climate change. This book, however, is not a reflection on India's role in international negotiations. Instead, it is an attempt to provide a bird's-eye view of how India has approached climate change in its policy response and what the debates related to domestic strategy to tackle climate change are. However, a brief discussion of India's position in international climate negotiations is necessary to put India's domestic policy in context.

Multiple narratives and conversations exist about the challenge to India posed by climate change from different points of view. All of them are not equally dominant in the mainstream discourse on climate policy. Depending upon how one frames the threat from climate change in Indian context, one may also consider some of them less important, at least for the time being. This book describes some of the perspectives impartially.

Because this book aims to impart information to the layperson, particularly from India, on the threats posed by climate change to Indian society and economy, such equidistance from different perspectives is warranted. It is hoped to excite the interests of the reader to initiate a larger public conversation about climate change rather than propagating an academic prognosis on the subject in Indian context. Accordingly, a conscious effort has been made to avoid information overdose and present a logically consistent story without oversimplifying or diluting the scientific facts. Reflection on perspectives, of course, is difficult to protect from the meanings different readers assign to the jargon and syntax used in conveying the message. As a reader of different perspectives, I am not immune to this unique autonomy of language. I have tried to use words in their most common and basic senses unless the meaning, or the sense, is extremely contextual.

The discussion presented in this book is organized into three parts: (1) a brief introduction to climate change as a policy problem, an outline of what it means to India, and India's approach to this problem in a global context; (2) a summary of India's domestic policy so far to deal with climate change; and (3) some key contemporary issues that India must engage with in designing its climate policy.

Climate change: a scientific perspective

Climate change refers to the impact of increased concentration of GHGs (greenhouse gases) in the atmosphere in the long term, usually understood as a pattern over a period of 30 years. Various economic activities and ecological processes contribute to the emission of different GHGs into the atmosphere. These gases stay in the atmosphere for many years. Hence, regular emissions of these gases increase their concentrations in the atmosphere. As the concentrations increase, the earth's capacity to trap the heat received from the sun increases. This greater capacity raises the average temperature of the earth's surface. Such warming of the earth is referred to as global warming. It is important to remember that global warming refers to the rise in annual average surface temperature, including winters being extremely cold or summers being moderate.

The main economic activities that contribute to the emissions of GHGs include burning fossil fuels such as coal, oil, and gas, agriculture and allied activities, and the destruction of forests in terms of area as well as quality. Since these activities are primarily carried out by people – the Anthropocene – the emissions are called anthropogenic emissions. Historically, these are the activities that have propelled the growth of human civilization and the modern economy, also referred to as the industrial society. This is particularly true of the post-Industrial Revolution period since the mid-18th century, which has seen unprecedented increase in industrial output, transport of goods and people, and urbanization driving the exponential growth in the exploration and consumption of fossil fuels. A synthesis of physical and social

3

science research using IAMs (integrated assessment models) informs us that unrestricted anthropogenic activities causing an increase in the concentration of GHGs in the atmosphere will lead to a change in climate that would be detrimental to the survival of our current industrial economy and society alike (Figure 1). To put the threat in perspective, various scientific assessments estimate that by the year 2100 the temperature of the earth's surface is likely to rise, compared to that during the pre-industrial revolution period, by between 2.7 °C and 5 °C with the current level of policy commitments by different countries, whereas the globally agreed Paris Agreement aims to limit the temperature rise by then to 2 °C (and aspires to 1.5 °C). In contrast to these estimates and global policy objectives, the annual average surface temperature has already risen by 1 °C since the Industrial Revolution. It is alarming to note that much of this rise in temperature has occurred during the last five decades. In sum, the global policy response is grossly inadequate compared to the goal it has set for itself. Even if the aspirational goal of the Paris Agreement is achieved, the world would still need to adapt to a temperature rise of 1.5 °C.

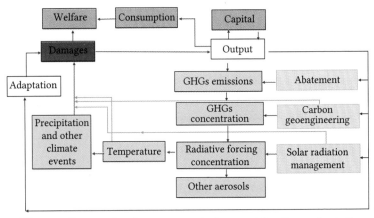

Figure **1** Interaction between emissions, mitigation, adaptation, and economy

Not only the economy and climate change but also various responses to climate change are dynamically linked, raising multiple dilemmas for those making policies related to climate change (Figure 1). At the heart of the economy is the well-being of people derived from and measured by the level of consumption of goods and services. Production (and distribution) of goods and services needs resources, including energy, technological systems, financial resources, and human and institutional capacities. The more we consume, the more we need these means of production. But more production (and distribution) implies more consumption of fossil fuels for energy, causing more emissions of GHGs, thereby accelerating global warming. In the previous two sentences, 'distribution' is put within brackets deliberately to underscore that it is an afterthought, and often ignored, in the policy discourse on climate change. We are faced with two choices: we either adapt our economy and social life to the impacts of global warming (adaptation) or avoid the need for adaptation altogether by striving to limit, reduce, and eventually eliminate the increase in the concentration of GHGs in the atmosphere (abatement or mitigation). In the likely event of inadequate mitigation, we will need to adapt to the impacts as well as to mitigate them, simultaneously.

As Figure 1 further illustrates, if the emissions of GHGs from the production process are not abated, we will be caught in the vicious circle of constantly increasing levels of temperature, the ever-changing climate, and the ever-increasing, and dynamic, need to adapt to the changing climate and the adverse impacts of those changes. Hence the first and the most important response to the threats posed by climate change is to decouple production from emissions, broadly known as abatement or mitigation. Theoretically, it is also possible to reduce the concentration of GHGs in the atmosphere even after they are emitted by anthropogenic activities. The use of carbon geoengineering technologies such as carbon capture (from the atmosphere) and sequestration (CCS) or utilization (CCU) or nature-based negative-emission technologies such as bio-energy and greater afforestation can help us lower the concentrations in the atmosphere. It is also theoretically possible to manage the influx of solar irradiation into the earth's atmosphere by using solar radiation management technologies such as artificial clouds or increased concentration of aerosols in the upper layer of the atmosphere. These technologies reflect sunlight from the earth's atmosphere and reduce the influx of heat itself, thereby limiting the effects of GHGs. These theoretical solutions, however, are only complementary to decoupling the emissions of GHGs from economic activities and will be needed when we fail to reduce the emissions. Hence, these options are referred to as 'Plan B'. The need to adapt to climate change, theoretically, should be limited to the impacts associated with the concentrations of GHGs after implementing mitigation measures, including carbon and solar geoengineering. However, the deployment of mitigation measures and their collective effect globally are uncertain processes, and hence the goalpost for adaptation too is uncertain. Put simply, we do not know if we should adapt to an ultimate scenario of global warming of 2 °C or 4 °C. The lower the mitigation effort, the greater will be the impacts of climate change—hence the need for adaptation.

Authoritative estimates of the impacts of climate change are to be found in the reports of the IPCC (Intergovernmental Panel on Climate Change), an international scientific body that synthesizes latest scientific research to help policymaking primarily at the global level. So far, six assessment reports have been published by the IPCC, the latest being in 2022.

The impacts of global warming manifest themselves in two forms: slow-onset events and extreme events.

Slow-onset events are those that occur at a very slow pace over a long time and their impact is more permanent. These include a rise in the global average surface temperature, melting of arctic ice and glaciers, rise in sea surface temperature, rise in the sea level, changes in the pattern of precipitation, ocean acidification, desertification, salinization of soil and groundwater, and reduced availability of freshwater. The slow pace can be understood by the fact that the global average surface temperature has risen by about 1 °C over the 270-year period from 1750 to 2020. However, as the concentration of GHGs in the atmosphere increases, so does the pace of change. These slow-onset events affect different aspects of social and economic life and vary across different sectors and countries depending on the extent of rise in the temperature (Box 1).

Box **1** Impacts of temperature rise (°C), by sector: 1980–1999

Water
- Increasing availability of water in moist tropics and at high latitudes
- Decreasing availability of water and increasing drought at mid-latitudes and semi-arid low latitudes
- Millions of people exposed to increased water stress

Food
- Increasingly complex, localized negative impacts on smallholders, subsistence farmers, and fishers
- Post 1 °C rise, tendency for cereal productivity to decrease at low latitudes; post 3.5 °C rise, reduced productivity of all cereals at low latitudes
- Post 1 °C rise, tendency for productivity increase in some cereals at mid- to high latitudes; post 3.5 °C rise, productivity decrease in some regions at mid- to high latitudes

Coasts
- Increasing damage from floods and storms
- Post 3 °C rise, steady disappearance of about 30% of global coastal wetlands

---

- Post 2 °C rise, increased annual frequency of coastal flooding due to cyclones and storms

Ecosystems
- Post 1.5 °C rise, up to 30% of species at increasing risk of extinction; post 4 °C rise, significant extinctions around the globe
- Increased coral bleaching with temperature rise: post 2.5 °C rise, widespread coral mortality
- Post 2 °C rise, terrestrial ecosystems become sources of carbon instead of sinks of carbon; 15%–40% of ecosystems to be affected; ecosystems to change
- Increasing species range and risk of wildfires

Health
- Increasing burden of malnutrition, diarrhoea, and cardio-respiratory and infectious diseases
- Increased morbidity and mortality from heat waves, floods, and droughts
- Changed distribution of some diseases
- Post 3 °C rise, substantial burden on health services

SOURCE IPCC Fourth Assessment Report, 2007

Extreme events, on the other hand, are those climatic events that occur rather randomly – the so-called outliers in the overall pattern of climatic conditions – with great intensity and immediate impacts. These include heavy rainfall causing floods, long spells of dry days causing droughts, heat waves, cold waves, cyclones, and storm surges. The impacts of these events are relatively easy to understand and predict. They usually cause significant losses including the loss of human lives, damage infrastructure, and disrupt routine life until reconstruction and rehabilitation are undertaken. With the advancements in weather forecasting models, the increased accuracy of early-warning systems has made it possible to prepare for such events and minimize losses. The main concern related to extreme weather events is the unpredictability of their frequency and intensity. Although there is consensus among scientists that with an increase in global warming such extreme weather events will be both more frequent and more intense, it is difficult to predict them. This makes choosing adaptation strategies particularly difficult.

We have articulated the kind of interlinked choices of policies related to mitigation and adaptation we must make to address the challenge of climate change. The defining challenge is the uncertainty of its impacts and a rather indeterminable effect of mitigation efforts in the long term. These uncertainties eventually make it difficult to assess the adequacy of adaptation measures. Overall, the choices of policies on climate can be an under-reaction or an over-reaction to the scale of the challenge. That is what makes climate change a wicked problem.

How should India be concerned about climate change?

Climate change concerns countries primarily from the standpoint of adaptation needs and mitigation efforts.

Climate change poses a range of risks to the population and economy and it is imperative for a country to adapt, that is to lower the risks and to be prepared to live with them. Risk is a combination of the degree of exposure to climatic conditions such as intense rainfall or heat waves, the vulnerability of a community or sector being exposed, and the preparedness to deal with the vulnerability. Exposure depends on location and vulnerability is influenced by such factors as location, livelihood, gender, and access to welfare infrastructure. The ability to deal with vulnerability depends on technical knowledge and capacity, financial resources, and institutional capacity. It should be obvious therefore that risks vary with communities, sectors, and countries, depending on the extent of exposure to climatic variations, their vulnerabilities, and their preparedness. A country with greater exposure, higher vulnerability, and lower preparedness is obviously at a higher risk. Accordingly, a country can determine whether it should be concerned about adapting to climate change.

The second approach to dealing with climate change is mitigation, that is to avoid the risks emanating from climate change by reducing or controlling the emissions of GHGs in the atmosphere. A country that emits more GHGs should in principle have greater opportunities for mitigation. Countries that do not have high levels of emissions of GHGs at present but are likely to increase the levels in pursuit of economic development in the future have the option of following an alternative development path that leads to comparatively low levels of emissions—the so-called low-carbon development pathway.

The choice between mitigation and adaptation is not mutually exclusive. Countries may – and in many ways should – be concerned about climate change from both perspectives. India is one such country. The importance of India's intervention in addressing climate change emanates from the fact that India is both among the largest victims of climate change as well as a major player in addressing it. Depending on how one frames the problem, the primacy of these facts changes. For those who emphasize lowering the emissions of GHGs as a primary response to climate change, mostly the international political community, it matters the most that India is the world's third largest emitter of GHGs and therefore India is essential to the solution. On the other hand, for those who emphasize the impacts of climate change on peoples' lives what matters the most is that India is a vast country with many vulnerable climatic zones and home to a large number of people extremely vulnerable to climate change. At the crossroads of these two extreme perspectives is the view that economic growth is essential if countries are to have enough resources to adapt to climate change and be resilient to it. Depending on accessible technologies, particularly in the energy sector, economic growth could be an emission-intensive pathway and may worsen the climate crisis or it could be a low-carbon development pathway. Access to technologies depends on the ability to pay for them and the capability to adopt them. India has been at this crossroads ever since the negotiations on climate change began at the UN General Assembly in the late 1980s.

In climate negotiations, India has long maintained that its per capita emissions, as well as historical contribution to the concentration of GHGs in the atmosphere, are significantly lower than those of industrialized countries, which also have the technological and financial resources necessary to achieve the required reductions in emissions. Hence the primary burden of reducing emissions falls on the industrialized countries and not on India and other developing countries. It is the industrialized countries whose historical emissions have led us to the crisis. India's priority is to ensure that the vast majority of its citizens have resilience to climate change. India was ranked 7th in terms of risks from climate change by Germanwatch's global climate risk index, 2021. The sheer size of India's population, let alone the existing inequalities and regional and sectoral vulnerabilities, makes the magnitude of the risk a primary concern for the country. For example, the effects of climate change potentially expose the 36 different agroclimatic zones of India to erratic spells of rains during the south-west monsoon with extended intermediate dry spells, thereby increasing the risks from climate change. A resilient country should build a climate-resilient infrastructure as well as alleviate poverty, even if it means higher emissions in the short term. The developed countries should shoulder the burden of creating this time window of opportunity for the developing countries before lowering emissions can become their priority.

However, the choices for India are more complicated. For a large and growing economy in which the bulk of infrastructure building and industrialization are yet far away, carbon lock-in or creating stranded assets is a real risk. Most of the infrastructure and industrial units have been operational for 30 years or longer. With proper repair and maintenance, their life can be extended. Because that requires high upfront investments, it is economically difficult to retire such units prematurely, especially for a country with scarce resources. Early retirement of infrastructure or industries would mean having assets that produce no economic value. It is important, therefore, that building new infrastructure and industrialization are aligned with low-carbon development pathways. Otherwise, India will be saddled with emission-intensive infrastructure and industries for a long time, which would pressurize India even more to take drastic measures in the future to address climate change or to step-up its efforts at adaptation. India, therefore, needs to make dynamic choices related to technologies, infrastructure, and industrialization that meet its immediate goals of economic development but at the same time also allow some flexibility to embark upon a rapid decarbonization pathway when such technologies become easily accessible.

India's choices for adaptation are even more complex than those for mitigation. Unlike the choices related to mitigation, those related to adaptation are linked with the degree of risk, which varies over time and with the extent of rise in temperature. The frequency of extreme weather events, for example, is linked to temperature rise, which is inversely related to the extent of mitigation efforts. It is feared that with lower mitigation efforts, resulting in greater rise in temperature, extreme weather events such as cyclones, heat waves, and extreme rainfall would be more frequent: a once-in-a-century event could occur two times or three times in a century. This implies that infrastructure built to withstand an extreme event that occurs once in 10 years – covering about 40 years of its life – would no longer be resilient to climatic variations. Should we then plan for an event that occurs once in a decade or once in a century? This type of choice is fundamentally different in terms of cost and scale than that involving mitigation, such as which to promote, renewable energy or energy efficiency. The choice is further complicated for a rapidly urbanizing country with a growing population, particularly of urban poor, and with ever-increasing population density. India has a long coastline home to a huge population and industrial infrastructure vulnerable to cyclones, storm surges, extreme rainfall, and sea level rise. Yet, more than half the population depends on agriculture spread across 36 agroclimatic zones, each vulnerable to climate change in different ways. It is both easy and difficult at the same time, therefore, to consider the urgency of undertaking an aggressive resilience-building programme. However, scientific literature estimates that with current policy commitments by countries on a global scale, the temperature rise could range from 2.7 °C to 5.4 °C. As Box 1 indicates, this range makes planning adaptation measures extremely difficult and yet all the more urgent.

In addition to the risks resulting from physical changes in climate are risks from the measures adopted to respond to climate change, which too need careful consideration. A simple way to understand such risks is to divide them into two categories, namely (a) risks that result from global governance of climate change and (b) risks that occur due to national climate policy. International responses to climate change primarily impact the prospects of a country in the international market. For example, a collective decision by several countries to move away from fossil fuels would adversely impact the incomes of countries exporting crude oil as well as refined oil in the form of petrol and diesel. India being a net exporter of refined oil products faces this economic risk in the light of commitments made towards mitigation by its export partner countries. Similarly, the global investment market is turning sharply away from emission-intensive technologies and towards low-carbon technologies. Global rating agencies undervalue businesses that rely heavily on fossil fuels. These global developments introduce risks of reduced access to international markets and finance if a country delays embarking upon a low-carbon development pathway. However, at the national level, such embarkment can lead to the risk of reduced economic competitiveness in the international market because of the high cost of shifting to low-carbon production processes. These scenarios can make a population more vulnerable economically, invariably affecting its ability to prepare itself to face climate-related risks.

The size and diversity of its economy, geography, and population place India in a precarious situation where at every step multiple trade-offs must be considered. Despite India's long-standing position in international negotiations of the primacy of adaptation, India needs to be worried about climate change not only from the perspective of first-order imperatives of mitigation and adaptation to climate change but also from the second-order imperatives of managing risks that emerge from policies to face the challenge of climate change. It is obvious, therefore, that India has to opt for a multipronged dynamic strategy to address the challenge.

India and the global politics of climate change

Global politics of climate change revolve around two concerns, namely share in the burden of dealing with the problem and expectations from countries in terms of climate action in the context of their national circumstances.

Addressing climate change includes both mitigation and adaptation measures as well as provision of the means to implement those measures including financial resources, technology development and deployment, and capacity building. The major issues in sharing the burden are (1) the amount of reductions in emissions in absolute terms that a country should undertake and (2) the entity that should shoulder the responsibility of ensuring that the necessary means to achieve those reductions are available to all countries, particularly to the developing and least-developed countries.

The second concern relates to the special circumstances and aspirations of countries related to climate action expected from them. How would the climate commitments of a country impact its national interests? Here, national interests mean domestic pressures and priorities of socio-economic development and stakes in the international economy through trade and competition.

Together, the response to these two concerns can potentially alter the domestic political economy and global positioning of economies. No wonder climate change has been such a sticky and slow-moving case of global cooperation. One must bear in mind that other recurring concerns in academic literature or media debates about global politics of climate change, such as the 'polluter pays' principle, differentiation, equity, finance, and technology transfer, are either different framings or part of the response to these two concerns.

India's contribution to shaping the global politics of climate change can be understood at three levels.

First, the very framing of the climate crisis as a development challenge is owed to India. In 1972, Indira Gandhi, being the only head of state attending the Stockholm Conference other than the host Sweden, set the tone of global environmental politics by emphasizing the overriding priority of socio-economic development and poverty eradication and the sovereign right of countries over their natural resources. Later, when the UNFCCC (United Nations Framework Convention on Climate Change) was being negotiated in the early 1990s, India played a pivotal role in drafting the terms of global cooperation. India prepared a draft text of the UNFCCC, which was later adopted and submitted by the G-77 and China as their position during the negotiations. The draft reasserted the framing of global environmental politics from a developing-country perspective, held the industrialized countries accountable for their past destruction of the environment, and demanded that industrialized countries take the responsibility for building global capabilities to change the course of development. This is best reflected in the articulation of Article 3.1 (Principle of equity and common but differentiated responsibility and respective capabilities) and Article 4.7 (Overriding priority of eradication of poverty and socio-economic development for developing countries, and mitigation by developing countries being subject to developed countries fulfilling their national and international commitments on climate change).

Second, India defended the broader interests of the developing and the least-developed countries in the negotiations. In 2010, when, for the first time since climate change negotiations began, Ambassador Chandrashekhar Dasgupta was not part of the Indian delegation to the COP (Conference of the Parties), one negotiator from an African country remarked that Ambassador Dasgupta was like a wall behind which smaller nations felt safe during negotiations. While the Western media has often painted India as a country standing in the way of progress, India has ensured that climate action does not become an instrument for further marginalization and impoverishment of nations in which the world's poor live. In fact, India has time and again exposed the farce of good intentions presented by many industrialized countries. For example, in 2008 India challenged the industrialized countries by saying that India would be willing to commit to never exceeding the per capita emissions beyond 2 tonnes CO_2 equivalent per year if the industrialized countries commit to bringing down their emissions in this direction. This remains to date the boldest intention on climate action by any country. However, the industrialized countries failed to take up the challenge, and India has rightly taken the wait-and-watch approach to committing to climate action on international platforms while setting ambitious domestic targets. Many other developing countries too have followed the same approach.

India was part of a small group of countries, namely Brazil, China, India, South Africa, and the USA, that played a pivotal role in breaking the political deadlock in a global agreement on climate change in Copenhagen in 2009, which eventually paved the way for a bottom-up climate regime expressed in the Paris Agreement of 2015. Setting up the GCF (Green Climate Fund), with a quantified collective obligation of the industrialized countries to provide the requisite finance, and the CTCN (Climate Technology Centre and Network) were the long-standing demands of developing countries that were materialized in the Copenhagen Accord. Although many have argued that the accord compromised on the principle of differentiation and released the industrialized countries from their historical responsibility by agreeing to a pledge and review based on global cooperation, it can also be argued with equivalent force, along with the benefit of hindsight, that the pragmatism of the accord has made progress on global climate action possible. Moreover, by not fulfilling the financial obligations related to the replenishment of the GCF the industrialized countries stand more exposed in their hypocrisy than ever.

Third, and in my opinion the most important, contribution that India has made to global cooperation on climate change lies in continually upholding the sanctity of global climate agreements and of the moral principles and pragmatic concerns underlying those agreements. Throughout the negotiations, India has been firm on making sure that the moral foundation of equity in climate agreements is not lost altogether. As a matter of fact, the Paris Agreement notes that the concern for 'climate justice' is important for only 'a few' countries. India's is the only NDC (nationally determined contribution) that bring up the matter of justice upfront. Pragmatically too, India stood firm on its commitment to the Paris Agreement when the fear of a race to the bottom loomed large in the light of the USA's withdrawal from the Paris Agreement immediately after it was signed. More important, India innovatively launched the International Solar Alliance during the Paris COP together with many other countries, including France. The alliance is arguably the most pragmatic technology-centric initiative in global cooperation on climate change, and many industrialized countries remain exposed once again as they are yet to join the alliance even after seven years of its existence.

The discussion above is broadly concerned with the issue of burden sharing. Arguably, concerns about the impacts of climate action on national economies are embedded in the positions taken by countries during negotiations at international platforms. Yet, the various dimensions of the impacts of measures to deal with climate change within a country as well as across geographical boundaries are not clearly defined. The UNFCCC, in principle, protects developing countries from the ill effects of climate policies implemented by other countries, including restrictions on access to global markets. However, in a free-market global economy, the chain of impacts is long and complex: for example, it is difficult to determine the impact of climate policies in Japan on the development prospects of India or the climate resilience of Indian cities. With the exception of a few explicit cases such as the proposed border carbon adjustment tax in the European Union, a measure that India has strongly opposed, it is not always easy to determine a country's position or role. This is an area where India should play an active role in tracking the climate policies of major industrial economies and the potential impacts of those policies on the developing and the least-developed countries. It is likely that the evolving national climate policy landscape in industrialized countries can open up new opportunities for learning and economic diversification. At the same time, the opposite is equally likely. It is quite possible that the consequences of a synchronized climate policy in the industrialized countries, even if unintentional and unforeseen, may force Indian economy to adapt early to the changing global market (for example, the transition to electric vehicles) or make Indian ecosystems vulnerable (due to geoengineering solutions adopted by other countries, for example). There is a gap in such assessments globally. Given the similarities that India's population and its economy share even partially with a diverse set of developing and least-developed countries, India should ideally lead the way to such assessments and monitoring.

The landscape of adaptation policy

Adaptation to changes is an age-old process. Throughout the history of human civilization, communities have adjusted to, and pursued innovations to survive and prosper under, varying conditions. Failure to adapt has led to irreversible losses. Yet, what makes adaptation to climate change different from past experiences is the probabilistic knowledge about the changes in climatic conditions and the impacts of such changes on the human environment in the future. This gives societies an opportunity to plan to avoid or minimize losses and, if possible, benefit from those changes. Such planning is informed by an understanding of the relationship between the vulnerability of a community or system to a particular change, exposure of the community to that change, and the adaptive capacity (the ability to withstand impacts in the event of exposure) of the community. Higher vulnerability and exposure coupled with lower adaptive capacity place communities at a greater risk. The overall aim of the policy related to adaptation is to minimize risk by way of managing vulnerability, minimizing exposure, and building adaptive capacity.

As Box 1 illustrates, major concerns related to adaption to climate change emanate from the probable impacts on the sectors such as water, agriculture, and health and the locations – the tropics, coasts, and mountains – that define human well-being, including security. The fact that exposure to changes in climatic conditions will vary in intensity and frequency across geographies and sectors makes adaptation both geography specific and sector centric. Broadly, a given sector faces similar vulnerabilities to climate change, but different geographies compound, moderate, or intensify them. Because it is the vulnerability that necessitates adaptation, most adaptation policies tend to be sector specific. The variations are informed by differences in the adaptation capacities of communities and the scale of exposure. It is taken for granted that certain aspects of adaptation such as access to information, education, and income levels are independent of sectoral vulnerabilities and geographical exposure.

The landscape of adaptation policy in India comprises three types of interventions.

First is obviously the stated national policies for adaptation. These are primarily the missions aimed at specific outcomes of adaptation under the NAPCC (National Action Plan on Climate Change), implemented by the sectoral nodal ministries, on sustainable agriculture (Ministry of Agriculture), water (Ministry of Jal Shakti), the Himalayan ecosystem (Department of Science and Technology), forestry (Ministry of Environment, Forest and Climate Change), urban habitat (Ministry of Housing and Urban Affairs), health (Ministry of Health and Family Welfare), and strategic knowledge on climate change (Department of Science and Technology). Some of these missions also aim at outcomes of mitigation. Broadly, the missions aim at promoting practices that make the relevant sectors less vulnerable to climate change or increase their capacity to withstand changes. For example, the National Mission on Sustainable Agriculture promotes the use of alternative cultivation practices such as organic farming, efficient irrigation techniques, watershed management, and new varieties of crops resilient to variations in temperature, rainfall, water salinity, drought, and so on. The mission on the Himalayan ecosystems and that on strategic knowledge on climate change are characteristically different from other missions as their primary purpose is to better understand the needs for policy interventions related to climate change.

The second type of policy interventions related to adaptation comprise a diverse set of sectoral policies and programmes and local projects primarily oriented to provide stable welfare measures to communities. The interventions are implemented by such diverse actors as ministries and departments of the state, civil society organizations, multilateral organizations such as the World Bank and the United Nations Development Programme, and bilateral agencies such as GIZ (Gesellschaft für Internationale Zusammenarbeit, the German agency for international cooperation) and SIDA (a similar agency of the Swedish government) in partnership with local government units, community-based organizations, private-sector interventions (commercial activities and those aimed at discharging corporate social responsibilities), philanthropic foundations, and autonomous government agencies (for example NABARD and the National Disaster Management Authority), etc. Various initiatives under the Ministry of Rural Development and the Ministry of Road Transport and Highways offer very good examples. The spread of quality road networks to remote areas has increased the general adaptive capacity of India significantly. This network has significantly minimized delays in providing health services, evacuation, relief material, and reconstruction services in the event of climatic disasters. The Mahatma Gandhi National Rural Employment Guarantee Act has been used innovatively in some instances to build resilience infrastructure at the local level. The act guarantees a minimum income to poor households giving them opportunities to adapt to adverse circumstances. Many small-scale interventions in water-scarce regions, such as rainwater harvesting and integrated watershed management, have enabled vulnerable communities to manage their lives despite scarce resources.

The third type of interventions, arguably the most important in the long run, are the state action plans on climate change (SAPCCs) adopted by every state and union territory during the past decade. Two aspects make the SAPCCS critical for adaptation, namely (1) the priority accorded by the state governments to adaptation in their overall outlook towards developing the SAPCCS (although mitigation measures were not excluded from the plans) and (2) the stated mainstreaming of climate change imperatives into state development plans, which emphasize sectors that are most relevant to development planning of a state. Because several sectors vulnerable to climate change are invariably the responsibility of the state government, state development strategies are a natural home for the interventions related to adaptation. Structurally, the SAPCCS serve as the bridge between national adaptation interventions and projects implemented by other actors, including local government units.

Having outlined the policy landscape and the general direction of adaptation policies in India, let us now turn to some aspects that need attention for improving the quality of adaptation planning. At the granular level, every sector and region require more rigour and comprehension in policy design and implementation; however, at the macro level, three aspects are worth deliberating on.

First is the concern that a policy should not be an example of maladaptation—which can happen when an intervention aimed at adaptation turns out to be a contributor to vulnerability or limits the scope of adaptability. The causes for this outcome are the overlooking of multiple vulnerabilities and inaccurate assessment of exposure. Communities are vulnerable in different ways and in different contexts, such as social, economic, environmental, and regional. If a community is vulnerable in more than one context, the risk that it faces increases. This is understood as the intersectionality of vulnerability. Further, the intensity of exposure varies with time, making it difficult to predetermine the likely level of risk that one has to prepare for. Mapping the outcomes of vulnerability, exposure, and adaptation to a combination of vulnerability and exposure is essential for an effective adaptation policy. In many instances, adaptation policies or programmes lack such mapping, introducing some uncertainty in the adequacy of the adaptation to address probable changes in climatic conditions in the future. Barring a few examples of states and cities that made detailed scientific assessments of risks and arrived at informed interventions, such as the strategy to address urban floods, most of the interventions aimed at adaptation are based on past experience.

The second aspect that requires attention is to take a second look at the scope of vulnerabilities that require adaptation measures. Some areas have received little attention in adaptation strategies. For example, vulnerabilities of energy industries and transport infrastructure, which are widely considered mitigation sectors, have been grossly overlooked. The level of awareness among the stakeholders is low. Many assessments of corporate governance with respect to climate change and sustainable development, such as those based on the ESG (environmental, social, and governance) framework or the Task Force on Climate-related Financial Disclosures, find that reporting of climate-induced risks to physical infrastructure, business outlook, and financial prospects is poorly understood and the topics are inadequately reported. There is progress, but it has not been enough: it is important to realize that there has been little policy push towards recognizing vulnerability and the need for adaptation measures in these sectors.

The third aspect relates to the proliferation of initiatives based on community-based adaptation, which has received a great deal of attention worldwide over the past two decades. Although examples of such initiatives are many, they are by and large driven by civil-society organizations and international initiatives. For a country as diverse and as large as India with complex intersectionality of vulnerability, it is perhaps important to have a stronger institutional push for such efforts. True, concepts such as micro-credit and self-help groups have become regular features of the annual budget, but beyond money, a dedicated institutional framework is likely to go a long way. To begin with, it would be good to have a system of evaluation recording the processes, responses, and outcomes related to all initiatives and interventions – or at least those based on community-based adaptation – aimed at adaptation. It would help improve the planning and implementation of those measures.

Climate change mitigation in India

Two facts have influenced India's international stance on mitigating GHGs emissions. First, India has always been among the so-called major emitters given the size of its economy. Second, India's per capita emissions have been among the lowest and continue to be so. Accordingly, India needed to balance these two extremes while formulating its international policy. At home, however, India's mitigation strategy has been straightforward and has evolved organically within the context of industrialization and concerns of energy security. From day one it was clear that addressing climate change would require fundamental changes in energy systems. The framing of climate change as essentially a developmental issue logically implied that the path to address climate change must be an energy pathway consistent with the imperatives of development, predominantly defined in terms of increasing industrialization. This in fact predates the climate change debates. In the aftermath of the oil crisis of 1973, India had already decided to pursue alternative energy sources and energy efficiency. More serious efforts in this direction were made during the 1980s when international cooperation on wind energy and modernization efforts of industry to promote energy efficiency were launched in an institutionalized manner. India's response to mitigation measures has been a continuation of these early efforts and relies heavily on the promotion of alternative energy sources and energy efficiency.

The centrality of carefully managing the energy sector is also derived from the fact that per capita energy consumption,

and the resultant emissions of GHGs, are directly proportional
to the Human Development Index. A minimum level of energy
consumption is required to attain a decent level of well-being.
It is not surprising therefore that when India announced its
formal climate policy in its NAPCC in 2008, an overall co-benefits
approach, promotion of renewable energy (particularly the
National Solar Mission), and energy efficiency were the mainstay
of the plan's mitigation component. Even the mission focusing
on urbanization (National Mission on Sustainable Habitat) is
significantly linked to the promotion of renewable energy and
energy efficiency. The only exceptions, arguably, are the missions
focusing on forestry and sustainable agriculture—spheres in which
non-energy-centric activities lead to lowering the emissions. It is
important to note that the legal foundation of mitigation in the
energy sector rests in the Electricity Act of 2003 and the Energy
Conservation Act of 2001, dating prior to the NAPCC.

Balancing the triad of energy–development–emissions
obviously continues to steer India's mitigation strategy even
at the international level. In 2010, when India agreed for the
first time to communicate an economy-wide mitigation plan
as part of the Cancun pledges, India articulated it in terms of
lowering the emission intensity of its GDP by 20%–25% below
the 2005 levels by 2020. This articulation carefully asserted that
development, measured in GDP terms, would remain the priority,
and the aim would be to contain the emission-intensive energy
consumption required to attain a higher level of development.
In other words, it was a socio-technical pledge to achieve a
higher Human Development Index with a relatively low energy
consumption. Later, in 2015, the articulation of the nationally
determined contributions (NDCs) in the Paris Agreement followed
the same language and set the target of reducing the emission
intensity of GDP by 33%–35% from the 2005 levels by 2030.
Obviously, renewable energy, energy efficiency, and forestry-
based interventions remain the core of these international pledges.

The commitments are further elaborated as sectoral targets of ensuring that 40% of the installed capacity of power generation is based on fuels other than fossil fuels and creating an additional cumulative carbon sink of 2.5 gigatonnes of CO_2 equivalent in the forestry sector. The latest pledge made in 2021 at COP 26 to make India a net-zero-emissions economy by 2070, is an extension of past strategies and would require a more dynamic strategy. This issue is discussed later in the section titled 'India's net-zero target: the context and road ahead' in detail. Recently, India updated the NDC targets to reducing emission intensity of GDP by 45% and installing 50% of non-fossil fuel-based power generation capacity by 2030. A national campaign, namely LiFE (Lifestyle for Environment) to bring about lifestyle changes has also been announced as a part of updated NDCs.

At home, India has been more aggressive with sectoral targets. For example, despite the snail-paced progress on solar power until the drafting of the NAPCC, the National Solar Mission set an ambitious target of achieving 20 GW of installed capacity by 2022. This was further increased to 100 GW in 2014 when the actual realization was only around 1 GW. Not only that, the target for wind power was also set at 60 GW by 2022. To facilitate the achievement of these targets an ecosystem of regulations and incentives was created. The incentives included various subsidies and exemptions from duties and long-term contracts with producers guaranteeing them a fixed tariff per unit of power generated, the so-called feed-in tariff, as well as a generation-based incentive. Another incentive was in the form of RPOs, or the renewable purchase obligations, which makes it mandatory for electricity distribution companies to buy electricity generated from renewable sources up to a stipulated percentage of the total electricity distributed by them. These obligations were further facilitated through a market-based instrument, namely renewable energy certificates, which can be traded and used to fulfil the above-mentioned obligations. These efforts have yielded mixed results. Although India is a long way from achieving these domestic targets, progress has been impressive in terms of total installed capacity and growth in investments in the renewable energy sector. The performance, however, is less than satisfactory in the case of compliance with the renewable purchase obligations; it seems that the obligatory instruments have not worked well compared to the incentive-based instruments.

The story of promoting energy efficiency has been qualitatively different. To begin with, since the mid-1980s energy intensity of the GDP has been steadily declining. This decline is partly because of technological advancements that accompanied new investments, particularly in the service sector, the share of which in the economy has increased significantly over the last three decades. The service sector tends to be less energy intensive than the manufacturing sector. In the manufacturing sector, the efforts of the Bureau of Energy Efficiency, empowered by the Energy Conservation Act, 2001, have paid off. Unlike the targets for renewable energy, those for energy efficiency are based on technological feasibility and financial viability. The efforts are aimed at surmounting behavioural and institutional barriers. A combination of obligatory, incentive-based, and awareness-oriented mechanisms has created the momentum for the demand and supply of energy-efficient products as well as their production process. A mechanism to make consumers aware of how energy efficient a given appliance is, namely a rating system in the form of the number of stars for various appliances consuming electricity, has encouraged not only consumers to buy more efficient products but also the manufacturers to continue offering more efficient products. Incentives for energy efficiency have been particularly innovative, aimed at removing barriers through handholding, trust building, and market creation. The business model of the Bachat Lamp Yojana to promote efficient lighting is a unique example. The scheme allowed consumers to adopt energy-efficient lamps that were beyond their purchasing capacity through financial handholding and created a large enough market for manufacturers, by aggregating the demand for such lamps to bring down the cost. Another example is the perform, achieve, and trade scheme, which combines mandatory energy-saving targets for selected industrial units with incentives for overachievement by trading the additional energy saved through energy-saving certificates and also addresses financial obstacles by introducing a partial risk guarantee fund. One innovative idea was to exclude the consumption of renewable energy while calculating the energy intensity of production (specific energy consumption) of a given unit, which promoted the use of renewable energy. All these efforts have created an institutional ecosystem and a behavioural choice narrative favouring energy efficiency.

The progress of mitigation efforts in the urban, forestry, and agriculture sector has been a chequered one. Policies related to cities have emphasized making buildings more energy efficient through such voluntary instruments as the GRIHA rating system for 'green' buildings, improved waste management, promotion of mass transit systems such as metros and bus rapid transit system and, more recently, promoting electric vehicles and related infrastructure. The success of these interventions varies from city to city. In any case these efforts overlap those that promote renewable energy and energy efficiency. The IPCC assesses that globally, in developing countries, the urban development process has to go a very long way for the world to be consistent with a pathway compatible with a 1.5 °C rise in temperature. This holds true for Indian cities as well. At present, one can only be optimistic about the fact that urban policy and planning in India has begun to learn from, and replicate, successful interventions from other cities, and a blueprint of what a low-carbon city would look like is almost ready.

India has consistently resisted making any commitment or even pledge related to mitigation in the agriculture sector in negotiations because the country accorded priority to food security and socio-economic development; therefore, major interventions in the agriculture sector are not expected. Yet, the co-benefits approach is at work in mitigation-oriented schemes in the sector, however marginal they may be in terms of lowering the emissions. The more prominent interventions focus on using water and energy more efficiently, which would also lower the cost of production. Accordingly, the promotion of solar-powered energy-efficient irrigation systems has received significant attention. Indirectly, the spread of organic farming may also contribute to reduced consumption of fertilizers, which in turn would eventually help in lowering emissions. However, given the pressures of ensuring food security, this is a distant scenario.

The forestry sector has a tragic story. Conservation and improvement of forest resources have been an obvious and almost the first choice in addressing environmental challenges since the Stockholm Conference in 1972. India has introduced a slew of legal and policy instruments to this end. From the perspective of CO_2 mitigation, REDD+ is the dominant mechanism incentivizing performance-based payments to protect, preserve, and improve forests. (REDD is short for 'reducing emissions from deforestation in developing countries'; the plus sign, added later, stands for sustainable management of forests, conservation of forest carbon stocks, and enhancement of forest carbon stocks.) Although many REDD+ projects have been successful, India's performance, which is consistent with the global trend, in managing forest resources for CO_2 mitigation has been far from satisfactory. After more than a decade of the Green India Mission under the NAPCC, little information is available to demonstrate any credible progress. Moreover, the relaxations provided in the environmental impact assessment through the 2020 amendments are, according to many, a step backwards in protecting India's forests.

To sum up, India has made progress on the mitigation front in some sectors and is beginning to have a grasp of mitigation strategy in some others (Table 1).

Table 1 Emissions (million tonnes of CO_2 equivalent) of greenhouse gases from India (1994–2016)

Source	1994 First national communication	2000 Second national communication	2007 Second national communication	2010 Biennial update report 1	2014 Biennial update report 2	2016 Biennial update report 3
Energy	744	1027	1374	1510	1910	2129
Industrial processes and product use	103	89	142	172	202	226
Agriculture	344	356	373	390	417	408
Land use, land-use change, and forestry (LULUCF)	14	-223	-177	-253	-301	-308
Waste	23	53	58	65	78	75
Total (without LULUCF)	1214	1525	1947	2137	2607	2838
Total (with LULUCF)	1228	1302	1770	1884	2306	2530

India's announcement of mitigation targets at international forums

Cancun pledges (2010): Reduction in emission intensity of GDP by 20% from 2005 levels by 2020

Nationally determined contributions (2015)
• Reduction in emission intensity of GDP by 33%–35% from 2005 levels by 2030
• 40% of installed capacity to consist of non-fossil-fuels-based power by 2030
• 2.5 to 3 gigatonnes of carbon equivalent of additional carbon sequestration through forestry and plantation

Net-zero target (2021): India to become a net-zero emission economy by 2070

Updated nationally determined contributions (2022):
• Reduction in emission intensity of GDP by 45% from 2005 levels by 2030
• 500 GW of installed capacity based on non-fossil-fuels-based power by 2030
• LiFE: a mass movement to nudge individual and community action to preserve the environment

Many meaningful lessons can be drawn from the experience of the last two decades. It can be argued that India perhaps does not need to look outside for success stories. Instead, a reflection on failures as well as effective interventions within would yield meaningful insights for the future course of action. The most important of the lessons would relate to how the private sector and communities have responded to government interventions. Government agencies have time and again pointed out that the financial and the human capacities of the government are limited. Hence, involvement of the private sector and of communities is important for attaining a higher level of targets. How much involvement works in Indian context, therefore, must be reflected upon with utmost objectivity and care. What can be said confidently is that India would need to deploy a mix of instruments including mandatory targets, removal of disincentives and barriers, incentives and handholding mechanisms, and awareness.

The capacity challenge to implementation

India has argued for long that support for capacity building is essential for developing countries to act effectively on climate change. Lack of capacity has been identified as one of the major challenges for India too. The 6th Assessment Report of the IPCC categorically calls for the need to build institutional capacity to achieve global as well as national goals on climate change. Both mitigation and adaptation broadly require three categories of capacities, namely those of implementation, technical, and institutional.

The capacity to implement relates to the ability to mobilize the necessary means – particularly finance and technology – essential for implementing any project. Over the years, the developed countries have been reluctant even to promise to provide finance and technology on terms favourable to the developing countries let alone delivering on any such promises made. In 2010, at the

Cancun COP, the developed countries had pledged to provide public finance (in the form of grants) to support developing countries. The support was to increase to reach 100 billion dollars per year by 2020; however, this promise remains unfulfilled so far despite the fact that the Paris Agreement permits climate finance accounting to include sources other than public finance and the use of other instruments of funding in addition to grants. The Government of India recently announced that as much as 85% of the finance for implementing climate policies and projects in India has been mobilized through domestic sources.

The technical capacity relates to the ability to assess and identify suitable projects and policies relevant to climate change and to implement them efficiently. This in turn involves the ability to identify the kind of projects or policies needed to achieve specific objectives, to choose appropriate and cost-effective technological options and their sources, to estimate the financial requirements and to think of ways to mobilize finances at the least cost, and so on. Usually, these capacities are embedded in human resources, which are scattered among different organizations, governmental as well as non-governmental. These skills also play an important role in using available financial resources more efficiently. In that sense, technical capacity tops the mere availability of finance and technology. Over the years, as stated earlier, India has made noticeable progress in building technical capacity. However, these capacities are concentrated only in a few academic and research institutes, and within such federal agencies as the NITI Aayog. India struggles with technical capacity at the state and city levels. As a result, formulation of economy-wide strategies and implementation of centralized initiatives are the cornerstone of India's achievements in dealing with climate change, mostly focused on mitigation. It is in the decentralized conception and implementation of climate projects, related to both mitigation and adaptation, that India finds itself wanting in technical capacity. It is not surprising therefore that many international agencies and initiatives such as ACCCRN (Asian

Cities Climate Change Resilience Network), GIZ, and SWITCH-Asia (the largest SCP – sustainable consumption and production – programme supported by the European Union in South East Asia, South Asia, Central Asia, Mongolia and China from 2007 to 2022) play key roles in filling this capacity gap. However, it should be noted that fees paid to foreign professionals are estimated to form as much as 35% of the total financial support that India receives in the form of technical assistance.

The capacity related to institutions refers to the institutional architecture that regulates as well as facilitates building and utilization of the two categories of capacity, namely implementation and technical, discussed above. In simple words, institutions are the rules that everybody should follow, the standard and routine practices of working while interacting with others in the process. Usually, these rules lay down the procedures of conceiving and implementing policies and projects including the distribution and division of roles, responsibility, authority, and accountability of different actors within and outside government. Given that policies or projects require different agencies to work together, it should be obvious that the rules and procedures governing them should be smooth for effective implementation. If these are inconsistent, implementation is likely to be affected even if technical capacity and the means of implementation are available. In fact, one strongly criticized example of India's response to climate change is poor utilization, due to institutional ambiguity, of the finance mobilized through the carbon cess on coal. The name and the scope of funds thus collected were changed frequently. Very often, lack of coordination between different departments of the government is identified as a major institutional barrier. Sometimes the excessive burden of complying with the rules is also a concern. For example, accessing finance from the Green Climate Fund demands a degree of technical expertise even to understand the requirements, let alone to comply with them—expertise that many in the developing countries lack.

Although it is the combination of the three categories of capacity that is necessary for effective and efficient implementation of strategies to deal with climate change, institutional capacity deserves additional attention, chiefly because, over time, it can help to overcome any barriers imposed by inadequacies in the other two categories. Usually, building institutional capacity is the task of the state, which can use its power to enforce rules and regulations to make other actors fall in line. This does not imply that technical capacity within the state agencies and financial resources are not required to improve institutional capacity but suggests that the state can convene all the different actors that together possess the required capacities and then use all the powers at its disposal, including those of coercion if required, to build long-lasting institutional capacities, allowing a country to mobilize the technical, technological, and financial capacities scattered among diverse actors. After announcing the NAPCC, the Indian government not only involved many non-state and subnational actors in implementation – by simultaneously pursuing and coercing them through various mechanisms – but also revised, expanded, and created new regulations and introduced policy provisions to assist those actors. This role is reflected in the progress in institutional capacity on mitigation, even if it is only at the macro level. However, the same cannot be said of adaptation. Institutionally, adaptation is a state subject and is to be reflected in the state action plans. Although these plans were developed following broad guidelines from the central government, the plans, to a great extent, repackaged the existing development plans, reflecting lack of technical and institutional capacity. Moreover, ambiguous statements about finances for implementing the state plans and dependence on the central government for finance signal the states' poor financial capacity. This lack of a structured assessment and development of institutional capacity at state level has led some to see the evolution of India's policy on climate change as 'opportunistic'.

India needs to think hard about streamlining institutional capacity. Nothing explains this urgent need better than the challenges related to the availability of data. For a federal country, data must reflect the devolution of governance levels and overlaps of authority between the central government and state governments in different sectors. Consistency of data across different levels of government and under different heads of information is critical and badly needed. Several central and state agencies collect and maintain data related to different sectors and types of activity—each with its own methods and practices of collecting and presenting data. The multiplicity of methods makes it difficult to synthesize relevant information given the problem of reconciling different data sets before any valid comparisons can be made. The transaction cost of sourcing data from multiple agencies is high, limiting efficient use of the technical capacity available in different research organizations. For example, there is no mechanism to know how Indian cities are coping with different climate-related challenges. Information on different schemes of the central government related to cities is available, although not fully, from different scheme-specific sources. Even complete information on a given city is not available in one place. Designing an easy-to-access climate-centric data management system that can synchronize and synthesize data from different agencies at different levels of governance is critical to building institutional capacity to address climate change in India. With the stated objective of creating a 'digital India', such an undertaking should not be impossible.

Overall, what India needs to critically reflect upon is a reform in governance that aligns scientific concerns about the potential impact of climate change on development and ecosystems with the imperatives of institutional compatibility, scale, and coordination between different actors at different levels of governance. This requires a rearrangement of the responsibility, authority, and autonomy of different actors that may be difficult to achieve politically—nevertheless, it is essential.

Social objectives and climate policy

For a long time since the Stockholm Conference in 1972 the environmental agenda and developmental aspirations were at odds with each other. Global environmental policy debates were also seen as North versus South where the North, or the developed world, pushed the agenda of environmental protection to subvert the developmental aspirations of the South, or the developing world. It is not surprising therefore that the environmental policy narratives sought to moderate this tension. The concept of 'sustainable development' as given by the Brundtland Commission in 1986 offered a policy lens to recognize that social, economic, and environmental dimensions are of equal importance. The global climate policy agenda was outlined as an integral component of the pursuit of sustainable development at the core of which is the idea of intergenerational equity of opportunity for social and economic development along with a healthy environment. Article 2 of the UNFCCC categorically states that the ultimate objective of global governance of climate policy is to be achieved within the framework of sustainable development. Article 3.4 recognizes promotion of sustainable development as the right of all countries. Later, the introduction of such concepts as 'co-benefits', 'multi-criteria approach', 'sustainable development policy and measures (SD-PAMs)', 'green growth', and 'green jobs' should also be seen as an effort to build a narrative that lightens the tension between climate policy (mainly mitigation) and developmental imperatives. A thread common to all these policy narratives is the possibility that any intervention, be it developmental or environmental, can be designed in such a way that social, economic, and environmental imperatives are simultaneously complied with and that the goals related to climate and those related to development can be merged.

The synergy between adaptation to climate change and the pursuit of social and economic development has been broadly accepted. The chief argument is that economic development provides necessary resources to build adaptation capacity, and many of the adaptation concerns such as livelihood, health, food security, and physical security are integral to the idea of development. The developing countries, accordingly, maintained that their priority was adaptation. India, in the context of debate about mobilizing financial resources from climate action, had argued that as part of various social development policies, public expenditure is as much as 2% of the GDP. Progress on adaptation is therefore a yardstick of successful pursuit of climate policy.

It is the matter of lowering the emissions of GHGs that has been the arena for examining the trade-offs between climate policy and development goals. Mostly, the policy on mitigation has been driven by techno-economic modelling frameworks known as 'integrated assessment models (IAMs)'. As illustrated earlier in Figure 1, these IAMs examine the interaction between climate science and economics to suggest a range of policy options to tackle global warming. The defining knowledge base of these models is information about technologies, such as low-emission fuels for power plants and the cost of storage technologies or mass transport systems. These models help in exploring mitigation measures and economic scenarios of different policy choices such as carbon tax and investment push but have been criticized for being too abstract and for failing to capture the complex trade-offs that policymakers must deal with. Over the last few decades, therefore, the modellers have made efforts to develop more comprehensive analytical tools such as shared socio-economic pathways. To what extent these tools have helped in comprehensive policy design is yet to be examined.

As India has always prioritized social and economic development, it is only to be expected that the country's policy related to climate change will diverge from the development trajectory. Yet, many commentators, particularly from developed countries, point out, for example, the increasing quantities of emissions of GHGs from India. Many also point to the persistent vulnerabilities of India's populations and its economic system. Obviously, the purpose of such observations is to suggest that India has underperformed on climate policy and should adopt more aggressive measures. Although it is reasonable to see these pronouncements and interpretations as an effort to divert attention from the failure of the developed countries to fulfil their obligations, such selective interpretation of data on the emission or on the large number of vulnerable populations outside the context of balancing social development and climate goals itself is misleading. A reasonable assessment of India's ambition and performance on the climate front warrants a comprehensive evaluation of India's actions related to climate change and the country's development independent of any international comparisons.

India's progress on climate change in the context of social objectives can be assessed in two ways, namely (1) in quantitative terms, based on selected indicators, and (2) in qualitative terms, by looking at the policies and policy discourses for any relevant change in reconciling the goals related to climate change and the social imperatives of development.

The first way involves looking at indicators to measure change over time. For example, India's Human Development Index improved from about 0.5 to above 0.6 over the past decade. Early warning systems along with greater resilience in traditionally vulnerable areas have minimized the impact of extreme climatic events, particularly on human lives, significantly. Investments in renewable energy have reached 14.5 billion dollars in 2021/22, creating many job opportunities. Per capita income has also increased to 6000 dollars a year. Per capita electricity consumption has increased whereas emissions from power generation have remained almost stable. Moreover, India is way ahead of meeting its targets as given in its nationally determined contributions and has in fact raised the targets to 500 GW of power generation capacity from sources other than fossil fuels and a 45% reduction in emission intensity by 2030 compared to the level in 2005. These facts certainly mark noteworthy progress. Yet, overall, we find that India is yet a long way from ensuring access to clean and modern energy for all, creating sufficient employment opportunities, increasing the participation of women in the workforce, eliminating malnutrition, controlling distress migration from rural and semi-rural areas to urban centres, providing affordable health care, ensuring adequate access to potable water, extending the cover of social safety networks available to the vulnerable population, and so on. Broadly, India's progress seems to be characterized by improvements in macro indicators but a poor showing at the micro level. It is perhaps in building adaptation capacities at the micro (local) level through equitable access to development that India has underperformed.

The second way of assessing progress is to look at the policies, and policy discourses, per se and see if there is any relevant qualitative change in reconciling the goals related to climate change and the social imperatives of development. To begin with, this is a double-edged sword: on the one hand, at the macro level, one can find carefully drafted policy documents that recognize many possible synergies between policy imperatives whereas on the other, interventions on the ground, that is at the micro level, contradict those policies. Take for example the National Mission on Sustainable Agriculture, a well-intended policy document, which aims to reduce the vulnerabilities of the marginal farmers. Yet, the risks for them continue to increase. It is also quite possible that a policy does not mention many linkages explicitly. For example, the NDC document is broadly silent on many social-development-oriented SDG imperatives like gender. Yet, interventions such as Solar-Mamas are examples recognized the world over of mainstreaming gender into renewable energy. Moreover, the overlapping outcomes of different policies and programmes make it difficult to determine whether the desired changes came about solely as a result of conscious policy or were partly accidental. This problem of correct attribution makes any simple analysis difficult. Having recognized the challenges in making a comprehensive and qualitative assessment of policies, it is nevertheless possible to ascertain the thought processes behind policymaking.

The targets of a policy and the requirements of monitoring and evaluating that policy offer some insights into what is expected of the policy. And it is the explicit intentions of a policy that need to be assessed. For example, the Mission on Enhanced Energy Efficiency expects that the data to be monitored and reported cover only energy consumption, change in specific energy consumption, and the corresponding reductions in the emissions of GHGs—the mission does not explicitly ask for data on employment generation or health impacts of fuel-switching in industry. Seen from this perspective, India needs to go a long way in creating a system of framing policies that facilitates integration of social development benefits into interventions related to policies on climate change or vice versa. Building a commensurate system to measure, report, and verify data is an even more daunting task. Again, this is not to suggest that no provision of this kind exists; in fact, integrating green budgeting and gender accounting is now a requirement while framing many policies and programmes. However, these provisions are neither adequate nor apply across different policies and programmes.

To sum up, a credible assessment of the extent to which policies related to climate change and developmental imperatives (1) have been integrated and (2) are successfully implemented is hampered by inadequate data and their management. The problem is partly because policy design and its evaluation are not conceived to reflect these integrations in explicit terms at the outset. What India needs is to make its intensions of such integration clear in accordance with the 'co-benefits approach' of the NAPCC and gradually build a system of data management. In the absence of such a system, India will always be prone to

misleading assessments based on out-of-context assumptions
made by global researchers or data-generating agencies.

India's net-zero target: the context and road ahead

At COP 2021 in Glasgow, India's prime minister took the world
by surprise by announcing that India's target is to become a net-
zero-emissions economy by 2070. The surprise was primarily due
to two factors, namely that the developing countries were not
supposed to have a net-zero target under the Paris Agreement, and
India was expected to hammer-in the point that developed country
targets for net-zero emissions by 2050 were inconsistent with the
agreement.

The first factor was related to the Paris Agreement aims of
achieving emission neutrality at the global level by 2050 but
does not require all the economies to achieve net-zero emissions
by 2050. The argument of the historical responsibility of the
industrialized countries along with the principle of common but
differentiated responsibility and respective capability, which
India propagates very strongly, would imply that industrialized
economies should ideally achieve negative emissions by 2050,
compensating for the emissions from the developing and the least-
developed countries necessary for development in accordance
with their national circumstances.

The second factor was related to political strategy. In the past,
India had insisted on the immediate and short-term mitigation
by industrialized countries as a strategy against the pressure
to set medium- to long-term economy-wide mitigation targets.
The argument was strongly supported by the scientific logic
of the importance of early action as well as the political logic
of equity and climate justice. The stand was also justified by
the economic logic of the need to lower the cost of deploying
climate-friendly technologies for the developing countries
through early investments by the developed economies. In the
run-up to the Paris Agreement, after the USA and China had

made a joint announcement of their NDCS in January 2015, India was under tremendous pressure from the international community to match the Chinese pledge of not extending the country's peak emissions of CO_2 beyond 2030. However, India stood firm on not committing itself to any target for lowering emissions set in absolute terms; instead, India extended the relative target set in the Cancun pledge of reducing, by 2030, the emissions intensity of its GDP by 33%–35% from the 2005 level. In doing so, India continued to insist on enhanced targets for 2020 for the industrialized countries along with their obligations to support the developing and the least-developed countries in the form of funds, technologies, and capacity building. In fact, India was lauded by the Climate Action Tracker as the only major economy to make its NDCs compliant with the target of limiting the rise in temperature to 2 °C. When China announced its ambition to be net zero by 2060 in the run-up to the COP in Glasgow, India was under similar pressure. Many expected India to continue reminding the world that the 2050 net-zero goal of the Paris Agreement is a global aggregate, and the primary onus of achieving it is on the industrialized countries. Most important, India was also expected to underline the fact that the 2050 targets by the developed countries were inadequate because they had refused to respect the global goal of net-zero emissions by 2050.

Evidently, by announcing the target to be net zero by 2070, India let the developed world off the hook rather too easily. From the perspective of setting the narrative, it can be justifiably argued that this announcement cleared the way for focusing on implementation, and that the world would now watch the industrialized countries more closely to check whether they are doing enough to achieve their 2050 targets. However, that does not stop many developed-country commentators from labelling India as a laggard. Let us ignore them. They have been trying to show India in a bad light for decades and clearly do not care for 'climate justice': the Paris Agreement made it official that climate justice is important only for some (Parties)!

Let us now consider the implementation of India's target to be net zero by 2070. Considering the time horizon of about half a century and the rapidly changing technological landscape, it is not easy to plan or predict what the transition to net zero would actually look like. However, we can look at some of the modelling exercises to develop different scenarios depicting India's path toward a net-zero-emissions economy to assessing the smoothness (or otherwise) of the road ahead. While doing so, one must keep in mind that the outcomes of modelling exercises depend significantly on the assumptions the models make, the approximations that are built into the models, and the limitations of the models. In fact, the results should not be understood in deterministic terms as the numbers tend to look definitive; rather, as the term 'scenarios' asserts, they should be treated as the contours of probable pathways.

Taking a more pragmatic view, Table 2 summarizes the headlines as forecast for 2050 by some of the modelling exercises focusing on India's transition to a low-carbon economy consistent with the Paris Agreement. These results are consistent with the general logic that the transition would necessarily include decarbonization of the energy (particularly power) sector and electrification of the transport sector. Of course, energy efficiency would ease the burden of supplying adequate decarbonized energy, but a structural shift in the primary energy mix is the ultimate objective. Clearly, primary reliance on meeting 70%–88% of the demand for power through electricity generated from sources other than fossil fuels, particularly solar energy, by 2050 and a dramatic shift in favour of electric vehicles (70%–100% penetration) by the same year are unanimous conclusions of these modelling studies and have long been so. The new additions to the mix of options are green hydrogen as a fuel (13%–38%) and various combinations of biofuels and ccs (carbon capture and storage) technologies. In fact, many global modelling studies argue that without CCS, achieving the goals set in the Paris Agreement is impossible. India's path to being net zero is therefore as smooth or as uneven as the scope of diffusion of these key technologies in addition to greater penetration of energy efficiency in production and consumption. The status of these technologies in Indian context is seen in the S-shaped curve in Figure 2, which shows different stages in the life of technology from conception to R&D to deployment to saturation. The duration to complete this process, if timely institutional support is provided and market conditions evolve, is roughly 40–60 years assuming no technological glitches.

Table 2   Technology penetration (%) estimates by 2050 for net-zero emission target

Decarbonization measure	CEEW	IEA	IPCC	TERI/ Shell	CAT
Solar-based electricity, wind power, hydro power	83	88	70–80	88	73–75
Electric vehicles	80–84	90–100		70	100
Biofuels with CCS (carbon capture and storage)	62				
Hydrogen-based power	15	38	18	13	
Biofuels (without CCS)	98	41			
CCS	37				

Figure 2 suggests that for India the target of being net zero is a leap of faith in the uncertain technological future. Although solar photovoltaics, wind, and hydropower are mature technologies in the sense that their operations are well understood and investors do not doubt their feasibility, hydropower has little scope for

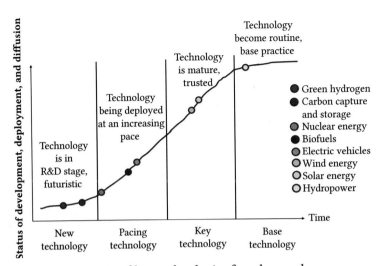

Figure 2 Status of key technologies for a low-carbon transition in India

expansion because of political and biodiversity-related concerns, and wind power has limited potential; solar power does have a huge potential but is constrained currently owing to lack of any large-scale storage technology. Research in storage technology has made remarkable progress in the past decade in terms of maximum battery capacity and cost, but has a long way to go to meet the requirement on a national level. One may assume that the maturity of solar photovoltaics will enable storage technology to leapfrog the S-curve once its capacity is satisfactorily demonstrated. Hence, it is reasonable to assume that India is likely to have a more or less smooth road to decarbonization of the power sector to achieve the target of being net zero.

India will face major challenges and uncertainties in the electrification of the transport sector, especially in scaling up the penetration of electric vehicles, biofuels, and nuclear power as well as commercialization of the emerging technologies of green hydrogen and CCS. Going by the logic of the S-curve, it will take at least 20 to 30 years for these technologies to reach the next stage in the life cycle of a technology, making it extremely difficult for India to deploy these technologies on a scale consistent with the scenarios outlined by modelling studies. A particular challenge to overcome the key barriers to progress of these technologies – except for biofuels – in India is the lack of indigenous technical know-how: nuclear energy faces international institutional and political barriers, and CCS, green hydrogen, and electric vehicles are technologies in which innovations are led by foreign companies. Indian companies have recently announced significant investments in R&D of green hydrogen, expecting a breakthrough in a decade. That is the best bet India has towards achieving the target of being net zero. Yet, one should not let two major needs out of sight: (1) humongous financial resources (over a trillion US dollars over the next three decades) and (2) institutional overhaul and technical capacity to build supporting infrastructure in time— two unfulfilled commitments of the industrialized world.

A just transition: difficult choices

Looking at the future, the question of how evenly the impacts of the transition to a low-carbon economy are distributed is bound to arise. Such concerns of fairness, or more generally of justice, arise mainly when the benefits or the costs of change are disproportionately distributed among different stakeholders, a phenomenon referred to as distributive justice. Climate change is a complex problem of justice because every level of choice of the measure to deal with climate change raises questions of justice. To begin with, the fact that the developed countries have contributed more to the concentration of GHGs in the atmosphere and have benefitted in terms of higher welfare levels and economic capacities. Developing, and the least-developed countries on the other hand are being denied these benefits, and not being compensated for it either. This discrepancy is at the heart of the problem of justice at the international level. In other words, the growth of the developed countries has come at a cost, namely the higher concentrations of GHGs—a disproportionate share of which is being borne by the rest of the world. Further, the failure to address this disproportionality in a timely manner would make the future generations disproportionately vulnerable to climate change and would be forced to make choices that current generations are unwilling to—yet another dimension of intergenerational justice. These concerns are recognized in the Preamble of the UNFCCC, the mother agreement on global cooperation for climate change: Article 3 of the agreement lays down the importance of the principle of equity in accordance with common but differentiated responsibility and the respective capability of countries in fairly distributing the cost of the measures to deal with climate change. Most important, the impact of the measures taken by one country on other countries is also subjected to the scrutiny of justice. However, this is only the tip of the iceberg. These foundational concerns are important and need to be considered while engaging in the debate on a just transition in Indian context.

The current debate about a just transition focuses predominantly on the centrality of moving away from coal. It is presumed that sooner or later, closing down of coal-based infrastructure from mining to power generation or burning coal as industrial fuel is inevitable. The chief concern of a just transition is the implications of this shutting down for people engaged in this sector and for their livelihood and welfare. The questions of new jobs for the workforce, protection against loss of jobs in future, re-skilling, and so on constitute the core of the just transition debate in the literature. In that sense, it is a concern raised by trade unions. Expectedly, this debate has gained momentum primarily in coal-rich developed countries for which this threat is more imminent and relevant, assuming that those countries will be the first to achieve net-zero emissions targets and should ideally become negative emission economies. It is therefore not surprising that the UK leads the Powering Past Coal Alliance. The questions are these: Should India think about the just transition focusing only on the transition of the workforce or should the just transition in countries such as India acquire a more comprehensive meaning? Why should the latter be the case of just transition deliberations in India?

In a globally integrated economy, no country can transition to a low-carbon future without being affected by what other countries choose to do. The domestic actions leading to a just transition therefore must be guided by two purposes, namely protection from the impact of actions of other countries and engagement with different facets of inequalities.

An example of the first purpose is the proposal by the European Union to introduce a border adjustment carbon tax. Although India would need to ensure, using diplomatic channels, that the EU does not follow through with this proposal at least in a manner that would affect India's access to EU markets, India would also need to plan to safeguard its industry should the proposal become a reality. More generally, other countries' long-term strategies for mitigation will impact India's economy, positively and negatively, and India needs to prepare to deal with those impacts. Change in trade terms alters the distribution of benefits among domestic actors: some sectors gain while other sectors lose. Ensuring that India's own long-term strategies for mitigation are not negatively impacted by such global developments is the first challenge to the just transition and may call for revisiting its negotiating strategies related to international trade, be it multilateral, plurilateral, or bilateral. The international trade regime, too, needs to transition to just and green trade regimes.

Some of the concerns related to the second purpose, namely engagement with different facets of inequalities, are discussed here. The inequalities are part of the global agenda of SDGs, or the UN sustainable development goals. Transition is a long-term plan involving the basic structure of core economic activities, particularly relating to energy and infrastructure, production and consumption patterns, and lifestyle choices. These are invariably embedded in the social distribution of inequalities and in the opportunities to change them. The inequalities encompass the economic status of different states and districts, the social and economic status of women, members of scheduled casts and scheduled tribes (communities assured of affirmative action by a schedule in India's constitution—hence the designation), and other marginalized groups and, most important, the intersection of vulnerabilities a specific social group is prone to. The current organization of the economy shows a recognizable pattern of who benefits and who is left out, and why. This pattern underpins various welfare schemes and policies aimed at more inclusive growth. Although many advocacy groups and scholars that support social justice have argued that many of these schemes and policies are ill-designed and ineffective, they nevertheless identify a pattern – perceived as unfair – of distribution of wealth, opportunities, and dignity. What happens to these patterns of unfair distribution once the economy goes through the transition is the essence of the just transition in India. Concerns of justice in a low-carbon economy cannot be different from those in the current economy but must be the same and evolve from what currently ails Indian economy and society. Some of these concerns are as follows.

Workforce transition and local economy

The coal sector is estimated to employ about 8 million workers formally and on contract. What happens to them and their families once the sector is pushed beyond the margins of the economy is an important question. Whole townships depend on coal-centric activities. Closure of mines, for example, may lead to utter economic destabilization of a mining town, also affecting the livelihoods of those who are not directly employed in the coal sector. Hence, although exploring the rehabilitation of affected workers to other sectors or ensuring a respectful retirement is important, keeping local economies alive is also integral to a just transition away from coal. One must also keep in mind the fact that the majority of the workers employed directly in the coal sector are on contract and many of them are women, although the share of women workers in the coal sector has declined over the decades. The job security of these workers is already precarious, making them generally vulnerable. What opportunities and support will they need for better and timely rehabilitation outside the coal sector? What is the scale of re-skilling required for such a large workforce? Do we have the means and capacity to do that in a short span of time? Who will, and should, finance this massive enterprise involving activities other than energy production and reducing emissions?

Regional disparity in resources

It just so happens that a significant portion of the total domestic coal supply comes from states in eastern India, which are also among the poorest states, Odisha and Bihar for example. Such alternative sources of energy as the sun and particularly wind, on the other hand, are more concentrated in western India, a relatively well-off region. A transition away from coal under these conditions means that the transition will benefit the already better-off states economically and widen the regional disparities between the eastern and the western states. The local economies of coal-rich states need a functional resilience strategy as a prerequisite to initiating the country's transition to a low-carbon economy. It must also be noted here that the eastern states have been more prone to extreme climate events in the past and are likely to suffer more as temperatures rise, making it even more important to think about adaptation and resilience before mitigation.

Mainstreaming gender into the new economy

The question of gender justice is mostly discussed in the context of vulnerability to climate change and building adaptive capacity. Women are either considered by default as the extremely vulnerable group or celebrated as a repository of knowledge and the frontline of resilience in the wake of disasters—rarely are they considered participants in creating a low-carbon future. In fact, the whole discourse of mitigation is heavily centred on technology and presented as independent of social concerns despite the NAPCC proclaiming that developmental co-benefits must underpin mitigation and adaptation strategies. The only opaque relationship that can be established is through references to such terms as green budgeting and gender budgeting, where one finds some overlaps. What is of even greater concern is that the Draft National Policy for Women 2016, which included a separate chapter on mainstreaming gender into climate policy, is yet to be formalized. One can take comfort from the fact that a reference framework is there to build upon, and the issue is delayed but not out of sight. This weak optimism is further challenged by the fact that the participation of women in India's workforce remains just about one-third of that in many developing countries with comparable per capita incomes. Given that India had recognized women as important drivers of economic growth as early as the 9th Five-Year Plan, more than two decades ago, the progress has been extremely slow.

Low-carbon transport (for whom?)

Relying less on fossil fuels for transport services is an integral part of long-term mitigation strategies in any country. Increasing the share of mass transit systems is an accepted way forward. Recent emphasis has been on the electrification of transport systems, particularly on increasing the penetration of electric vehicles. Clearly the emphasis has been on motorized mass transport systems and privately owned electric vehicles. Although these measures pose huge challenges related to infrastructure, concerns of justice should extend to those, particularly in cities, who use non-motorized privately owned modes of transport such as bicycles or walking. These are zero-emission options but do not get enough attention in planning urban infrastructure. By extension, the users of such transport services, who are largely from poor and marginalized backgrounds, are excluded from the discourse on, and planning of, low-carbon transport systems: they are assured neither a safe place on roads nor adequate budget for footpaths and cycle lanes.

Inequality and resilience

In the long run, India's climate policy needs to engage with the questions of reducing, if not eliminating, inequality as well as building resilience to climate-induced risks. Allocating all resources to facilitate the transition to a low-carbon economy would be a grave injustice to citizens if that economy is not also a climate-resilient one. Although some aspects related to resilience and mitigation have been mentioned above, albeit indirectly, a few specific aspects of vulnerabilities must be deliberated upon explicitly. The literature on vulnerability and resilience has unanimously opined that there are multiple drivers of vulnerability, with compounding effects, arguably the most important among them being unequal incomes. India faces the challenge of widespread inequality in incomes, making the bottom half or even more than half of the population extremely vulnerable to shocks emanating from climate change and other disasters. A large section of this vulnerable population is directly or indirectly dependent on agriculture for their livelihood. This combines their economic vulnerability with the vulnerability of the agriculture sector to erratic weather conditions and greater frequency of extreme events such as floods due to climate change. Add to that the potential trade-offs between land for agriculture and land for renewable energy plants, and we have another layer of vulnerability in the form of food insecurity in the pursuit of a low-carbon economy. The natural course of demographic changes implies that in a couple of decades, a large section of this vulnerable population will also be an aging population, making it even more vulnerable. The point, in brief, is that the just transition in Indian context should strive for a fair balance between mitigation efforts and building resilience to the impacts of climate change ensuing from a 1.5 °C to 2 °C rise in temperature, assuming the goals set out in the Paris Agreement are actually achieved.

In short, the imperatives of a just transition in India require simultaneous consideration of, and interaction between, fairness in international economic engagement and domestic implications of policy on climate change. At the same time, it is also necessary to strike the right balance between the imperatives of mitigation and those of adaptation to ensure a just transition. This would require significant technical preparation and analysis. So far, no structured and comprehensive assessment exists. The questions that confront a just transition in India, therefore, are these: Should we wait for a structured and comprehensive analysis? Should we continue the development-first with co-benefits approach? Or should we take some crude indicators of a multi-layered just transition such as gender-inclusive green jobs and enhanced social security net and move forward with policy feedback loops?

The not-so-changing landscape of climate governance

The latest IPCC assessment report has recognized the importance of building institutional capacity in achieving long-term climate goals. In other words, the report calls for better embedding of climate-policy imperatives into structures of governance. India is a federal polity in which the powers as well as responsibilities between the central government and state governments are clearly demarcated: the central list names areas in which the central government has exclusive power to make rules and policies; the state list details areas where the state governments have overriding power; and the 'concurrent' list describes areas in which the powers overlap. Through the 73rd and 74th amendments to the Constitution, such powers have been further decentralized to include local government such as municipalities and gram panchayats (village councils). Yet, the Indian federal system of government remains top heavy. In practical terms, the central government has more power over state governments in matters of implementation. Commentators on Indian federalism reason that this predominantly centre-driven character is due to several factors, chiefly by design given the inherent and continued inability at the subnational level but partly due to the relative concentration of and reliance on financial resources from the central government. To some extent, the dynamics of India's electoral politics have also contributed to this skewed concentration of power at the centre.

The top-heavy character of Indian federalism is best reflected in the way the governance of climate change has evolved in India. To begin with, climate policy was confined to the Prime Minister's Office, the Ministry of External Affairs, and the Ministry of Environment and Forests. Gradually, other sectoral ministries were involved, which eventually, in 2008, found a proper place in the framework under the NAPCC, which focused on such sectoral missions as the National Mission on Solar Energy (Ministry of New and Renewable Energy), Mission on Enhanced Energy Efficiency (Ministry of Power), Green India Mission (Ministry of Environment, Forest and Climate Change), Mission on Sustainable Agriculture (Ministry of Agriculture), the National Water Mission (Ministry of Jal Shakti), Mission on Sustainable Habitat (Ministry of Urban Affairs), and Mission on the Himalayan Ecosystem and the National Mission on Strategic Knowledge (Ministry of Science and Technology). The state governments, for a long time, had no specific role in determining climate policy and programmes although many sectors critical to the measures to deal with climate change (mitigation and adaptation) are either on the state list or on the concurrent list. Even when the state governments formulated state-specific climate policies and action plans on climate change (the SAPCCs), they did so under the guidance of the central government and followed the NAPCC formulated in 2008. The state governments did very little experimentation in drafting their action plans and mostly demanded funds from the centre, without specifying their use, giving credence to the perceived lack of technical and institutional capacities at the state level. Moreover, the SAPCCs needed to be approved by the central government, which reinforced the top-heavy governance of climate change. Nearly a decade later, when the SAPCCs were revised, it was once again under the guidance of the central government.

Clearly, the landscape of climate governance has expanded, mostly over the last 15 years, but the basic structure continues to be marked by top-heavy federalism. This pattern can be seen through two different, but not necessarily opposite, perspectives; although both see the evolution as a continuation of federal polity, they differ in what each considers as the drivers of specific aspects of this evolution.

The first perspective sees India's climate policy as a result of evolution shaped by prevailing needs and available possibilities within the existing governance structure to meet the demands of climate policy. This perspective makes the trajectory of climate governance in India to be somewhat 'opportunistic', arguing that climate imperatives are pursued only to the extent that existing governance framework permitted. The other perspective sees climate governance in India as progressing towards long-term development goals of energy security and industrialization, which are simultaneously aligned with and at loggerheads with climate imperatives.

The top-heaviness of changes in institutional embedding of climate policy in different ministries and state governments as governed by their mandates and priorities is primarily due to the structural responsibility of the central government to set national goals considering the constraints and capacities spread across different levels of government. In that, the trajectory of climate governance in India has been of gradual inclusion of more actors, 'calibrated' to an implicit understanding of consolidating concerns and implementation capacities of different actors.

One can speculate whether the long-term commitment of becoming a net-zero-emissions economy by 2070 would lead to a 'determined calibration' of climate governance in coming decades or the top-heavy federal approach would still be considered adequate. It is therefore imperative to look at some questions that should be addressed to implement the long-term climate targets effectively and to ensure that the targets are aligned with long-term development goals. At the centre of these questions are the new actors that should be included in the architecture of climate governance irrespective of whether it is seen as opportunistic or based on calibration.

Cities as centres of climate action

The projected increase in urban population (60% by 2050 in India) along with the required additional infrastructure is a matter of concern for mitigation and adaptation. Various assessments indicate that a large part of future emissions from the developing countries are due to the impending needs of energy services and embedded emissions in infrastructure yet to be built in cities. Urbanization would also increase the human impact of risks such as the urban heat island effect, heat waves, water scarcity, flash floods, heat waves, and cold waves given the greater population density in cities. Although this consideration necessitates strategic and scientific planning of urban development in India, the governance of cities should be facilitative of their needs to be low-emission and climate resilient.

Recently, many national initiatives such as the Smart Cities Mission have also pushed the cities to take mitigation-oriented actions, and international initiatives such as SWITCH-Asia too have facilitated such actions in some cities. With regard to adaptation, city administrations are institutionally informed of the guidelines issued by disaster management authorities at the national and state levels advising them to develop city-level disaster management plans. This directive, however, is not strictly enforced. Over the years, many international initiatives such as C40 Cities (a "global network of mayors taking urgent action to confront the climate crisis and create a future where everyone can thrive") and ACCCRN have encouraged and facilitated city-level actions to address specific vulnerabilities. Nevertheless, several cities have emerged as laudable examples of climate action in different sectors such as transport (Indore), waste management (Indore and Kochi), solar power (Chandigarh), water (Kanpur), heat stress (Surat), and resilience (Pune). The central question is, Has the governance structure been instrumental in building capacities for climate action in cities? The answer is a weak yes, at best. That some cities have been able to take effective climate actions is proof that the governance architecture is not a hinderance, as some believe. Yet, the evidence related to success stories alone tells a tale of lack of a foundation for governance. First, it is almost impossible to trace the evolution of these success stories through regular institutional mechanisms of transparency and accountability. Not even the international initiatives provide full details of the associated interventions to the public. Second, the institutional landscape in the better-performing cities does not seem to follow a pattern. Third, and perhaps the most important, the mechanisms of mobilizing and using financial resources for climate action in cities are rather ad hoc and project based.

In most cases, climate actions in cities are driven by spirited individuals holding public offices who manage within the existing governance system to create opportunities for climate action. In a few cases such as Surat, active civil society and industry associations have created an ecosystem for voluntary action. However, all this indicates a lack of technical and institutional capacity for sustained climate action, evident in ambiguity about how cities should deal with that lack. Mostly, it is left to the wisdom of city governments to conceive interventions without any authority to mobilize the means of implementation. Moreover, the ever-changing size and land-use pattern that many large cities have been experiencing pose a challenge to effective governance. It is therefore important to reconsider ways in which cities ought to govern themselves in the light of climate imperatives. City governance in India needs to relook at how cities can find a sustainable flow of finance consistent with their low-carbon and resilient development needs; how their technical and institutional capacities are built over time; and how they document and share their experiences for others to emulate to facilitate the overarching evolution of city governance in an informed manner. The question is, How much independent should Indian cities be to be ready to deal with climate challenge?

Corporations as drivers of resources

Increasing the share of private investments is seen as the key for scaling up climate action. Looking at the sustainability reports of large companies, one can note that many of them have either adopted quantified targets or policy direction to promote renewable energy and energy efficiency. The Carbon Disclosure Project, which seeks information from corporate houses on their climate actions, notes that Indian companies are increasingly willing to take climate actions and to making the information public. The sustainability reports, along with the annual corporate social responsibility reports, also reveal that adaptation, resilience, and sustainable development are increasingly becoming part of the routine activities of corporations. Recently, many independent agencies have begun to rate corporations on their performance in relation to ESG (environment, sustainability, and governance), making them favourably conscious of internal governance and public disclosures. Companies have begun to make efforts to improve their ESG ratings because they consider it important for brand building as well as for their investors. The most important impact, arguably, is due to the inclusion, or prospects of inclusion, in the perform, achieve, and trade (PAT) scheme that sets targets for companies in terms of energy savings.

In this process, companies have begun to build their capacities to align their business practices with the imperatives of climate change and sustainable development. Yet, detailed and specific information about individual companies' contributions to emissions of GHGs and the scope for lowering the emissions is scarce and hard to obtain. On many platforms, the representatives of companies have pointed out the need for clear guidance from the government about their roles and responsibilities, at least in terms of making data accessible in a consistent form. Although companies are aware of the expectations that they undertake mitigation activities, the awareness that climate change also holds potential risks for business infrastructure is poor. This lack of awareness is also reflected in the disclosure of financial risks due to climate change, weakening the transparent relationship between financial sector and industry in an uncertain climate.

Clearly, there is need for better aligning of businesses with the national goal of climate-resilient and low-carbon development. The business community has access to resources and possesses the technical capacity and the potential to generate useful and geographically disaggregated data sets from their operations. Such information is vital for effective planning and implementation. However, such aggregation of information will have to deal with issues arising out of the need for confidentiality and competition among businesses. Nevertheless, for a capacity-constrained country such as India, a more strategic system of corporate governance is required to improve efficiency in a time-bound manner. It is a difficult task. Yet, there have been examples of many industries engaging in a dialogue while drafting regulations based on understanding of mutual constraints and the need for hand holding in the larger interest. One example of such dialogue is the protracted consultation in setting targets for energy saving for selected companies under the PAT scheme. A dialogue with a clear agenda must begin, but the question is, What should be the agenda for that dialogue?

States as agenda setters

The importance of integrating social concerns into the just transition to a climate-resilient economy has been discussed earlier. From the perspective of governance, the nuances of such a transition are to be designed keeping in mind the specific trade-offs involved in each intervention at the local level. States therefore will have to be at the centre of setting the policy contours of transition because they represent an appropriate balance between scale and locality. The state action plans already provide a basis for implementing the national agenda aligned to the local context. However, what the SAPCCs currently lack is a comprehensive framework that brings together different actors, stakeholders, and their capacities. Answers to the following questions may help in arriving at such a framework.

- How can the private sector and civil society be instrumental in making cities climate resilient in an institutionalized manner?
- How can the states be innovative in mobilizing finance within the existing federal framework to support their SAPCCs?
- Do we need to think in terms of governance reforms more congenial to low-carbon climate-resilient state development?
- How do we build technical capacities necessary to conceive and implement appropriate climate actions within a state?

A coherent and climate-centric governance architecture would require replication of capacities at each level of the federal government including engagement of actors other than agencies of the state.

Another aspect that states would need to consider is that the impacts of climate change and ways to mitigate the adverse impacts respect no boundaries. Efforts are needed at regional level involving two or more states in implementation. This is particularly true for building resilience at the level of agroclimatic zones or large ecosystems spread across multiple states. Hence, a science-based governance is likely to be better compared than the current one centred around political boundaries. Of course, this is not to imply that the current architecture does not offer the required space for targeted and case-specific coordination between states but to suggest that it would perhaps be more efficient to design an institutional architecture that ensures long-term cooperation across sectoral, state, and technical capacities. In other words, voluntary and negotiated collaboration across state jurisdictions with sufficient flexibility should be institutionalized.

Polycentricity as aggregator of capacity

The foregoing discussion underlining the role of different actors, particularly their autonomy in making policy choices, defines polycentricity. The concept of polycentricity in governance recognizes the presence of multiple actors taking governance decisions independent of each other, driven by their voluntary initiatives. In doing so they are not accountable to each other. Yet, the commonality of goal makes them a part of a larger whole, without necessarily arranging them into a hierarchical relationship of authority and accountability. It implies that some actors are willing to make choices that the system does not mandate them to do. Polycentricity thus is a specific form of multilevel governance without hierarchies and associated accountabilities. Mostly, polycentricity emerges to address specific policy objectives or problems that may be temporary and immediate locally or for which a full-blown, permanent, and large-scale governance architecture is not required. Polycentricity introduces greater flexibility in goalspecific rules and mutual accountability between cooperating stakeholders.

In the context of climate change, capacity aggregation is arguably the most important driver of polycentricity. Several actors, national and international, are collaborating to implement initiatives related to mitigation or adaptation. The Global Climate Action Portal (originally known as the Non-state Actor Zone for Climate Action of the UNFCCC and launched in 2014) records many such initiatives across the world, including individual interventions and joint efforts by different types of actors on different scales. At present, the portal records 5 states, 69 cities, 12 investors, 252 organizations, and 267 companies in India involved in at least one such collaborative effort. Obviously, the actual number is likely to be significantly higher because many of the actors have not gone public. These collaborations bring together financial resources and technical capacities, many a time across borders. However, most of these initiatives are mainly in the form of projects. These initiatives provide useful institutional insights, yet the lack of an overarching governance framework overseeing these initiatives results in a situation where the congregation of capacities is rarely institutionalized. In some cases, efforts are not sustained or scaled up beyond the project life.

The emergence of polycentricity in climate governance in India is both an opportunity and a challenge. It is an opportunity in the sense that so many non-state and subnational actors are taking up initiatives to address climate change. In this process, they are not only bringing together diverse capacities depending on the needs of the intervention but also building their own capacities in governing climate interventions. In a sense, a bottom-up churning of capacity exploration is a process that the federal governance system can greatly benefit from. But herein lies the challenge of polycentricity. Because these initiatives are independent of each other, conceived of in pursuit of distinct climate-change related objectives by a diversity of actor types, a comparable and comprehensive database of these initiatives and their experiences is difficult to compile. It makes further integration of diverse capacities and institutional learning a distant outcome. It is even more difficult to steer these bottom-up efforts in a certain direction and at a certain pace. It is not surprising therefore that the literature documenting and analysing the effectiveness of polycentric climate governance increasingly recommends the need for orchestration or synchronization in tune with established governance frameworks. The question is, Who should be responsible for such orchestration and how should it be done?

Centre as a visionary administrator
In the light of the foregoing discussion, it seems natural that the central government will have to play a leading role in fine-tuning, if not reforming, the governance structure to better align it with climate change imperatives of development. This leadership, however, should be qualitatively different from the top-heavy federalism, aimed at gradually increasing the fluidity and flexibility in the system to accommodate the diversity of climate impacts as well as different capacities of actors to implement climate actions. The lack of capacity and ambiguous authority to visualize and pursue an alternative future among different actors make it necessary that the central government continues to shape the long-term vision. The task at hand goes beyond setting quantified targets to setting institutional processes that enables a dynamic collaboration between different levels of governments and actors on different scales of operation in a transparent manner. This exercise obviously will rely more on political vision for facilitative administration than merely following economic modelling tools for low-carbon transition. The question is, Will the political economy allow such an ideological churning? If not, what would change the political economy itself?

Conclusions
Climate change is often reported as a doomsday scenario. The threats it poses are undoubtedly grave. The choices it asks

humanity to make are complex and fraught with moral dilemmas, political compulsions, and capacity constraints. Yet, the way forward lies in being informed and considerate in making sensitive choices collectively. India is currently at that crossroads.

India has made a tentative but firm start on abatement of climate change over the last two decades and now has set eyes on a 5-decade long transformation of the economy towards becoming carbon neutral. This goal will bring about many changes in the socio-economic life of the country. It should also bring in innovations and, subsequently, an improved form of governance, more attuned to the goals of inclusivity. It is critical therefore to begin exploring scenarios of socio-economic changes that should accompany the necessary technological improvements. A managed change is rarely possible without acceptance by all sections of society. It is therefore important to initiate public engagement on issues of climate change. People need to make appropriate choices to push politics and markets towards a climate-resilient low-carbon development. The largest barrier to doing so would be the large gaps in income levels, social status, and economic opportunities. Hence, a sincere beginning is also needed for addressing inequalities as India embarks on the path to being a net-zero-emissions economy.

Stepping up adaptation planning and implementation can mark such a beginning towards addressing inequality. India, and the global community, should strive for an equal and resilient order with the expected launch of a global adaptation goal later this year at COP 27. For India, a national adaptation plan on climate change would be an entry point. So far, successful interventions have been scattered geographically and have been only theoretical at the sectoral level; they need to rise to the next level, to a clearly articulated national strategy based on vulnerabilities and response measures.

This new beginning should also be accompanied by necessary means of implementation. An action plan spelling out the means for capacity building, a budget, and the required financial and technical assistance must be prepared and shared with other stakeholders. A just net-zero goal would be a giant leap forward. It is important to make sure that all components are working at full capacity to implement and can withstand the often-unwarranted international pressure.

Bibliography

Allen M, Antwi-Agyei P, Aragon-Durand F, Babiker M, Bertoldi P, Bind M, Brown S, Buckeridge M, et al. 2019. Technical summary: Global warming of 1.5 °C. An IPCC special report on the impacts of global warming of 1.5 °C above pre-industrial levels and related global greenhouse gas emission pathways, in the context of strengthening the global response to the threat of climate change, sustainable development, and efforts to eradicate poverty. Intergovernmental Panel on Climate Change

Atteridge A, Shrivastava M K, Pahuja N, et al. 2012. Climate policy in India: What shapes international, national and state policy? *Ambio* **41** (Suppl 1): 68–77 https://doi.org/10.1007/s13280-011-0242-5

Bhushan C, Banerjee S, and Agarwal S. 2020. *Just Transition in India: an inquiry into the challenges and opportunities for a post-coal future.* New Delhi: iFOREST.

CAT. 2020. *Paris Agreement Compatible Sectoral Benchmarks.* Climate Action Tracker. 70 pp. https://climateactiontracker.org/publications/paris-agreement-benchmarks/ and https://climateactiontracker.org/documents/753/CAT_2020-07-10_ ParisAgreementBenchmarks_FullReport.pdf

Chaturvedi V and Malyan A. 2021. Implications of a net-zero target for India's sectoral energy transitions and climate policy. New Delhi: Council on Energy, Environment and Water. 24 pp. https://www.ceew.in/publications/implications-of-net-zero-target-for-indias-sectoral-energy-transitions-and-climate-policy

Chaudhary A, Krishna C and Sagar A. 2015. Policy making for renewable energy in India: Lessons from wind and solar power sectors. *Climate Policy* **15**: 58–87
doi: 10.1080/14693062.2014.941318

Dasgupta C. 1994. The climate change negotiations, pp. 129–148 in *Negotiating Climate Change: The Inside Story of the Rio Convention.* Cambridge, UK: Cambridge University Press

Dubash N K (ed.). 2020. *India in a Warming World Integrating Climate Change and Development.* New Delhi: Oxford University Press

Dubash N K and Jogesh A. 2014. From margins to mainstream? State climate change planning in India. *Economic and Political Weekly* **49**: 86–95
http://www.jstor.org/stable/24481085

Eckstein D, Künzel V, and Schäfer L. 2021. *Global climate risk index 2021: Who suffers most from extreme weather events? Weather-related loss events in 2019 and 2000 to 2019.* Bonn: Germanwatch. 48 pp.

IEA. 2020. Global Energy Review: CO_2 emissions in 2020
https://www.iea.org/articles/global-energy-review-co2-emissions-in-2020

IPCC. 2018. Summary for Policymakers, pp. 3–24 in *Global Warming of 1.5°C.* An IPCC Special Report on the impacts of global warming of 1.5°C above pre-industrial levels and related global greenhouse gas emission pathways, in the context of strengthening the global response to the threat of climate change, sustainable development, and efforts to eradicate poverty. Cambridge, UK and New York, USA: Cambridge University Press.
https://doi.org/10.1017/9781009157940.001https://www.ipcc.ch/sr15/

IPCC. 2022. Summary for policymakers, in *Climate Change 2022: Mitigation of Climate Change.* Contribution of Working Group III to the Sixth Assessment Report of the Intergovernmental Panel on Climate Change [P R Shukla, J Skea,

R Slade, A Al Khourdajie, R van Diemen, D McCollum, M Pathak, S Some, P Vyas, R Fradera, M Belkacemi, A Hasija, G Lisboa, S Luz, J Malley (eds)]. Cambridge, UK and New York, USA: Cambridge University Press doi: 10.1017/9781009157926.001

Jörgensen K, Mishra A, and Sarangi G K. 2015. Multi-level climate governance in India: The role of the states in climate action planning and renewable energies. *Journal of Integrative Environmental Sciences* **12**: 267–283 doi: 10.1080/1943815X.2015.1093507

Michael K, Shrivastava M K, Hakhu A, Bajaj K. 2020. A two-step approach to integrating gender justice into mitigation policy: examples from India. *Climate Policy* **20**: 800–814 doi: 10.1080/14693062.2019.1676688

Mathur A and Shrivastava M K. 2015. The pursuit of sustainable development in India, pp. 83–95 in *Building the Future We Want*. New Delhi: AFD, IDDRI, and TERI

Mathur R and Shrivastava M K. 2017. INDC and low-carbon technology deployment scenarios: India, pp. 57–82 in Anbumozhi V and Kalirajan K (eds). *Globalization of Low-Carbon Technologies*. Singapore: Springer https://doi.org/10.1007/978-981-10-4901-9_3

Parry M L, Canziani O F, Palutikof J P, van der Linden P J, Hanson C E (eds) 2007. *Climate Change 2007: impacts, adaptation and vulnerability.* Contribution of Working Group II to the Fourth Assessment Report of the Intergovernmental Panel on Climate Change. Cambridge, UK: Cambridge University Press. 982 pp.

Pillai A V and Dubash N K. 2021. The limits of opportunism: the uneven emergence of climate institutions in India. *Environmental Politics* **30** (Sup 1): 93–117 doi: 10.1080/09644016.2021.1933800

Shell International and TERI. 2021. India: transforming to a net-zero energy system. New Delhi: TERI. 56 pp. https://www.shell.in/promos/energy-and-innovation/india-scenario-sketch/_jcr_content.stream/1617850096430/4dc1d51b4d29c3dfea47f0a57e9 eef62000a021b/india-transforming-to-a-net-zero-emissions-energy-system-scenario-sketch-report.pdf

TERI. 2018. *Preparing India's Oil and Gas Sector for Changing Climate*. New Delhi: The Energy and Resources Institute. 28 pp.

Upadhyaya P, Shrivastava M K, Gorti G, Fakir S. 2021. Capacity building for proportionate climate policy: Lessons from India and South Africa. *International Political Science Review* 42: 130–145 doi:10.1177/0192512120963883

Some useful websites

Climate Action Tracker (CAT)
https://climateactiontracker.org/

Global Climate Action (NAZCA)
https://climateaction.unfccc.int/

Our World in Data
https://ourworldindata.org/co2-and-other-greenhouse-gas-emissions